# Addicted to Energy Deficit

Your Neuroscience Based Guide to
Restrictive Eating Disorders

Helly Barnes

For the two people who were there and kept
believing in me, no matter what.
You know who you are.

# Contents

# GLOSSARY OF TERMS

**A**mygdala The region of the brain primarily involved in emotional processing. It's commonly thought of as the part of the brain that drives a fight or flight fear response.

**Basal Ganglia** A group of structures near the centre of the brain, of which the striatum is a key component. This is a key brain structure for movement, as well as learning, habit formation, cognition and emotion.

**Chewing and spitting** A habitual behaviour seen in people with restrictive eating disorders in which they chew food but rather than consume it will spit it out.

**Craving** An overwhelming urge to engage in a behaviour or use a substance. Feelings of irritability, anxiety or fear can arise with a craving for an addictive *drug* (which includes behaviours).

**Dopamine** A form of neurotransmitter which when released in the brain has a rewarding effect and is a key chemical in motivation and goal pursuit. Dopamine plays a critical role in addiction. Having the right levels of dopamine is important for the brain and body.

**Endogenous (or natural) opioids** A more general term for enkephalins and endorphins. These naturally produced hormones act in the same way as morphine and other opioid substances and can create feelings of euphoria, stimulating the brain's reward system.

**Endorphins and enkephalins** Naturally occurring hormones that are released by the brain and send messages through the body. They can relieve pain, reduce stress and improve mood and in this way are thought of as *feel-good* chemicals. These are more specific terms for natural opioids.

**Energy deficit** A physiological state in which the body has insufficient energy in relation to energy coming in and/or stored energy supplies to meet its requirements.

**Ghrelin** Often referred to as a hunger hormone, ghrelin is produced from the gastrointestinal tract and increases the drive to eat by increasing food thoughts, as well as triggering other appetite stimulating processes.

**Hyperphagia or extreme hunger** A physiological drive to eat extremely high amounts of food as a natural biological response to semi-starvation. Extreme hunger occurs when the body is in a state of energy deficit with insufficient fat and lean tissue stores in relation to the genetically determined level it requires. This is not the same as binge eating because with extreme hunger, people maintain a sense of control in whether or not they respond to it, whereas binge eating is defined by a sense of loss of control over eating a lot of food in a short space of time.

**Leptin** A hormone produced by fatty tissue that helps to regulate hunger by promoting feelings of fullness. Without enough fatty tissue relative to the body's genetic set point, normal feelings of satiation are lost until those fat stores are gained. Sufficient leptin is considered one of the most important factors in true appetite regulation.

**Metabolism** All the chemical processes that occur in the body or an organism to sustain life. These processes require energy so metabolism is directly linked to energy availability and use.

**Neural networks and circuits** Brain pathways made up of connecting neurons form into complete networks and circuits that drive particular habits, behaviours, thought patterns and beliefs. Any new learning is wired into the brain to form into neural circuits for that particular learning. Networks develop when the circuits for different behavioural and thought pattens frequently intertwine, whereby one action will precede or coincide with the other, so the circuits driving each become interlinked.

**Neuron** A basic cell of the nervous system that sends and receives electrochemical signals to other cells. The brain is made up of billions of neurons which connect to and communicate with one another to form circuits and networks driving habits, thoughts, emotions and behaviours.

**Neuroplasticity** The brain's ability to reshape and change in response to new learning and new circumstances throughout the lifespan and hence develop new habits and *unlearn* old ones. This is also commonly referred to as *rewiring*.

**Neurotransmitter** A chemical that is released by one neuron to communicate with the next. In addiction, dopamine is a key neurotransmitter.

**Overshoot or fat overshoot** A body fully recovering from a state of semi-starvation needs to gain excess fat supplies in order to be able to restore and repair all lean tissue stores and fully emerge from energy deficit. Once this has been achieved, the overshoot fat will naturally subside, with no conscious attempts needed to lose it.

**Pre Frontal Cortex (PFC)** A section of the brain located at the front of the frontal lobe (just behind the forehead). The PFC is the intellectual centre of the brain, responsible for regulating behaviours through planning, decision making and impulse control.

**Quasi Recovery** A term widely used in eating disorder communities to describe someone with an eating disorder who has made some progress to overcome it but remains very driven by compulsive habits and behaviours related to the pursuit of energy deficit, leaving them living a *half-life*.

**Rituals** A particular way of behaving or thinking that has high importance placed on it, with an associated drive to repeat it in the same way time and again. Rituals become habitual and so are often performed with little conscious awareness. In themselves, rituals can become part of wider addictive patterns and often serve as cues to full engagement in an addictive behaviour or drug.

**Set point theory** The understanding that every body has a largely genetically determined set point level for weight that it will fight to maintain. It is now understood that this relates to set point levels for fat and lean tissue stores that the brain recognises as minimally necessary for that individual to be in energy balance.

**Striatum** One of the biggest parts of the basal ganglia in the brain. The striatum plays a key role in reinforcement learning and the creation and entrenchment of habits and addictions.

**Synapse** A space between two neurons across which the two cells communicate with one another by the release and uptake of chemicals (also called neurotransmitters). Synapses are the connection between neurons that allow them to communicate and form wider pathways, circuits and networks.

# Introduction

In the past two decades, I've gained a lot of insight into eating disorders. My twenty-seven-year-old self—who naively believed that she couldn't possibly have developed *anorexia* because anorexia only affected teenage girls who want to look like supermodels—has been on quite a journey. Developing an eating disorder as an adult, going through traditional treatment cycles, to finally find my own path taught me so much. I now use my experiences, knowledge and professional skills to work as a coach with others who are in the process of overcoming an eating disorder.

Throughout the years, I've taken every opportunity to learn as much as possible about eating disorders, trying to uncover the truth behind the seemingly inexplicable and irrational thoughts, behaviours and compulsions an eating disorder creates. But I could never find an explanation that entirely fit with my experiences, and I was left with unanswered questions.

One thing that often struck me was that eating disorders and addiction have some very strong similarities in relation to how they manifest and their impact. Recently, my curiosity about this got the better of me, and so I decided to explore whether there is a relationship between eating disorders and addiction. The knowledge I gained left me in no doubt that eating disorders are a powerful form of addiction for which there is a credible evolutionary explanation. Now, with this new understanding, I have an insight into eating disorders that fits everything in relation to my own experience and what I have witnessed in others.

Traditionally, addictions had only ever been thought about in relation to substances, such as drugs or alcohol. This view is now changing, with increasing recognition that addictions can occur, with the same brain-based changes, to behaviours, without the need for any ingested substances. The most common examples of this and the first to be given recognition in the Diagnostic Manual for Mental Disorders (DSM-5) are gambling disorder and Internet gaming disorder [1].

When you compare the signs and symptoms of an addiction to those features common to people with eating disorders, the parallels are striking. There's also now research from the field of neuroscience examining what is happening within the brain when someone has an eating disorder which shows that eating disorders and addictions have very similar brain-based changes. This is particularly in relation to the chemical dopamine, which has long been understood to be a key player in the development and entrenchment of an addiction.

During the years in which I had an eating disorder, the drive to follow certain disordered behaviours and restrictive habits felt very addictive. Attempting to stop myself from following through with them seemed impossible, even when I knew that they were damaging my health, relationships and happiness. If I did try to stop myself from engaging in a compulsive behaviour, I would develop side effects, such as irritability, restlessness, anxiety, depression, agitation, headaches and even shaking—the same effects common to people withdrawing from well-known addictive substances and behaviours.

Through my work in the field of eating disorders, I have observed time and again that some of the most effective methods to overcome one are what you might consider an abstinence approach with an addiction.

This book contains some simple research science and subsequent theories about addictions, eating disorders and the neurobiological parallels between the two. Developing this knowledge has provided me with much greater insight into what eating disorders are and why they are so powerful. This model of eating disorders as a form of addiction meets the reality of life with an eating disorder more closely than any other theories or medical models I have yet come across. Therefore, I hope the information in this book also helps you to form a better understanding about restrictive eating disorders. If you currently have an eating disorder, I also hope that it will allow you more self-compassion as you come to understand why an eating disorder is so hard, although not impossible, to overcome.

Establishing greater insight into what eating disorders are from a brain-based and biological perspective, while also considering social, emotional, environmental and interpersonal factors, enables us to find the most beneficial approaches to overcome them. These approaches are explored in later chapters.

This book provides a lot of information, science and theories and translates these into steps you can take in your own process to overcome an eating disorder. For those of you who want even more practical advice, I have also written a complementary handbook called, *Aiming for Overshoot*, with more hints, tips and advice to apply as you move through the day-to-day process of overcoming the addictive nature of a restrictive eating disorder.

---

1. American Psychiatric Association. (2022). Diagnostic and statistical manual of mental disorders (5th ed., text rev.). https://doi.org/10.1176/appi.books.9780890425787

# Chapter One

---

# Clarifying a Few Things from the Beginning

T his book is about eating disorders and focuses on restrictive eating disorders. Restrictive eating disorders are the subtypes of eating disorder for which restriction through reduced food intake and/or purging behaviours—which can include exercise, self-induced vomiting, abuse of laxatives, diuretics, diet pills or enemas—is a significant feature.

### Terms Used in the Book

Throughout the book, I use the general term *restrictive eating disorders,* but on occasion there is mention of subcategories such as anorexia nervosa, atypical anorexia, bulimia nervosa or binge eating disorder. Where this is the case, it is due to reference of a particular research paper that has studied people who fit into that particular subcategory.

At times the terms *eating disorder* and *addictive disorder* are used interchangeably. *Addictive disorder* is a widespread term for any form of addiction, of which I believe eating disorders are one. *Eating disorder* is used to speak more specifically to this topic. This is the case more often than not because, after all, eating disorders are what the book is about!

I often reference the *drug* someone is addicted to or in pursuit of. The term *drug* is not only used here in relation to substances that are ingested. When discussing the *drug* for people with restrictive eating disorders, it relates to the state of energy deficit or rewarding behaviours that they are addicted to. In the same way, the *drug* for someone with Internet gaming disorder would be playing Internet games.

### Three Core Principles that Underpin the Book

1. You can have any type of restrictive eating disorder in any body shape, weight or size, and these factors are not an indication of how physically or mentally affected you are by the eating disorder. The information in this book is relevant to you if you have a restrictive eating disorder, no matter what your body composition.

2. Categorising eating disorder subtypes is often unhelpful. Eating disorders can and do evolve over time. You will develop

a range of compulsive behaviours, thoughts and emotions as a result of an eating disorder. The way these manifest can change. You can and very possibly will move between subcategories. For example, people commonly move between an anorexia nervosa diagnosis to bulimia nervosa. The current subcategories can create more misunderstandings about eating disorders, take focus from where it's needed and reinforce stereotypes. Therefore, I have chosen to refer to *restrictive eating disorders* throughout the book and the information provided relates equally to any *type* of restrictive eating disorder.

3. Restrictive eating disorders are not driven by a *fear of fatness* or *fear of weight gain*. This is an explanation for eating disorders that conveniently fits our modern Western culture, where weight loss or being in a smaller body is applauded. That is not to say, if you have a restrictive eating disorder, that you do not have some level of fear or discomfort to the idea of gaining weight. It is to say that restrictive eating disorders are not as destructive as they are because of this fear alone. Chapter 11 explores this topic in more depth.

· · · ● ●· ● ● · ·

# Current Diagnostic Categories for Eating Disorders

Before getting into the juicy sections of the book, I'll provide a brief overview of the current diagnostic subcategories of eating disorders that large parts of the medical world use today to aid diagnosis.

Eating disorders are categorised in the Diagnostic and Statistical Manual of Mental Disorders (DSM). This is the handbook used by many countries across the world to guide health professionals in the diagnosis of mental disorders. Within the latest version, DSM-5-TR, eating disorders are classified into different diagnoses depending on symptoms and presentation. These include:

- Anorexia nervosa (AN)

- Bulimia nervosa (BN)

- Binge eating disorder (BED)

- Other specified feeding and eating disorder (OSFED)

- Avoidant restrictive food intake disorder (ARFID)

There are a few additional subtypes, but the ones listed above are the most commonly diagnosed.

## Anorexia Nervosa

For an AN diagnosis someone needs to display restriction of their energy intake relative to their requirements, leading to a *significantly low body weight*. This is defined as a weight that is less than *minimally normal*. They also need to display an intense fear of becoming fat or gaining weight and an inability to recognise how low their body weight is or the severity of their condition.

The AN diagnosis is further classified into two subtypes:

**Restrictive subtype**, where the individual doesn't experience binge eating or purging behaviours but they do diet, fast and/or excessively exercise.

**Binge eating/purging subtype**, where the individual engages in recurrent episodes of binge eating or purging behaviours. The purging might be through self-induced vomiting, laxatives, diuretics or enemas.

## Bulimia Nervosa

For a BN diagnosis someone needs to display recurrent episodes of binge eating and recurrent purging behaviours to prevent weight gain. Purging can be through self-induced vomiting, laxatives, diuretics or enemas. It can also be as a result of fasting (restriction) or excessive exercise. Many people think of bulimia as the stereotypical purging through vomiting, but this does not need to be the case for a BN diagnosis. The person also needs to experience problems with body image related to their weight and shape.

What's different then between a diagnosis of AN with binge/purge subtype and BN? Very little other than the fact that a person with BN has a body weight that is considered in a *normal or above normal* BMI range, while AN is a person with a weight considered below *minimally normal.*

## Eating Disorders Not Otherwise Specified

This category is used for people who meet many of the diagnostic criteria for one of the other eating disorder types, which has a detrimental impact on their lives, but their presentation doesn't fit perfectly into another category.

One of the most common eating disorders comes under an EDNOS diagnosis. This is *atypical anorexia* (AAN). For a diagnosis of AAN, a person needs to have all the necessary criteria for a diagnosis of AN but *despite significant weight loss, the individual's weight remains within or above the normal range.*

Essentially then, people with AAN have AN. They are just as disabled, and the symptoms are having the same negative effect on them. However, because they are not *below normal weight* and we are still too focused on a misleading BMI system, people with this most common of all subcategories of restrictive eating disorder are labelled *atypical.*

While this label is being used for people with all the symptoms of AN who are in bodies that are not below a *normal range*, the stereotypical picture of AN as someone who is emaciated is only going to continue. The fact is that *atypical anorexia* is actually far more typical than AN when the current diagnostic criteria are applied. Despite the fact that an anorexia diagnosis is far less likely to be made in people with bodies that are within or above the *normal weight range*, it is already recognised that AAN is around three times more common than AN [1].

Atypical anorexia also has the same medical risks as anorexia seen in someone who is *below a minimally normal* weight. The impact of AN behaviours on a person's organs and overall physical function is just as significant and potentially life-threatening in a person in a suppressed but still *normal* weight range. Bone mineral density is also just as likely to be lost [23].

Surely it's time to remove current weight relative to BMI standards from the picture. If someone has lost weight so that their weight is suppressed, and they display all the signs and symptoms of AN, no matter what their current weight, shouldn't we apply the same diagnostic label?

**Avoidant and Restrictive Food Intake Disorder (ARFID)**

A diagnosis of ARFID is given to people who restrict their food intake, describe a significant lack of interest in food altogether, avoid foods based on their sensory experiences (for example, textures, tastes or smells) or show concern about *aversive* consequences of eating (such as fear of vomiting or choking).

This food avoidance results in significant weight loss and/or malnutrition and may necessitate a dependence on nutritional supplements. Individuals with an ARFID diagnosis do not express body weight concerns.

ARFID is a relatively new diagnostic category for an eating disorder, and the majority of cases are currently being identified in children. Young children, age ten years or younger, are more likely to be diagnosed with ARFID when presenting with restricted eating than they are with AN. There's also a recognised link between ARFID and autism, with estimates that around 21 percent of people with autism could experience ARFID. Genetic links have been found to ARFID which also strongly correlate it to the genetic risk of autism [4].

ARFID is a restrictive eating disorder. The person restricts their food intake to dangerous levels, resulting in weight loss that can leave them medically compromised. The reasons attributed for these behaviours differ from the criteria to meet an AN diagnosis, and so the individual's experience of the eating disorder is different. However, it's likely that what is happening within the brain of someone with ARFID is similar to that seen in other subcategories of restrictive eating disorders.

## Binge Eating Disorder (BED)

Binge eating disorder is diagnosed in a person who regularly binge eats. Binge eating is defined as eating within a two-hour window an amount of food *larger than most people would eat in a similar period of time*. This is a vague statement, but it's generally assumed that the binge episode would involve an extreme quantity of food in that two-hour window. The binge eating must also be associated with a feeling of lack of control when eating during the episode. With BED there are no compensatory purging or fasting behaviours as in BN. The BED criteria also leave out mention of any body image concerns or distortion.

A true BED diagnosis excludes people who do compensate for a binge eating episode by restriction, dieting behaviours or exercise. These people fall into the AN or BN subtypes. It's likely that many people who have a diagnosis of BED actually have a restrictive eating disorder, and it's the restriction that drives them to binge. Therefore, if you do have a BED diagnosis, it might not be accurate if the binge eating episodes you experience are actually driven by restriction or other compensatory methods. The level of restriction does not have to be extreme, in terms of food amount or type, to trigger your brain and body to respond by driving a binge. If this is the case for you, then you have a restrictive eating disorder, not true BED.

A true BED diagnosis does fall outside the category of restrictive eating disorders and beyond the focus of this book. However, there is a lot of research to indicate that BED is driven by addictive behaviours. Therefore, later sections exploring the theory of addictive models for eating disorders are still relevant.

There are also other eating disorder subtype diagnoses in the DSM. The above information highlights the most referenced and the symptoms someone needs to present with for a diagnosis of these. Despite the lack of detailed reference to some of the other subtypes of eating disorders, I don't mean to invalidate them or anyone's experience of them. Anyone who has an eating disorder diagnosis not listed above is by no means excluded from the information in these pages.

### The Problem with the Current Diagnostic Categories

The current diagnostic categories for eating disorders are problematic because a lot of people move between the subtypes over time, even though they still have the same eating disorder. For example, 50 percent of people with a low weight anorexia diagnosis move to a diagnosis of BN [5]. Clearly these people have gained some weight and so no longer fit the AN binge/purge subcategory but otherwise still have an active restrictive eating disorder.

Similarly, someone with low weight AN, without binge/purge symptoms, who gains a small amount of weight but continues to experience the same thoughts, restrictive eating and related behaviours will move to a diagnosis of AAN under the current diagnostic criteria.

It's also not uncommon for people to move between diagnoses of BN and BED, either due to the cessation or uptake of purging behaviours while continuing to have binge eating episodes.

People with ARFID can develop a concern over their body weight or shape or a *fear of fatness*, which is a characteristic of AN, and subsequently have their diagnosis altered. When this occurs, they are then diagnosed as ARFID "Plus."

Perhaps we do need a way to indicate the more prevalent symptoms that someone with an eating disorder is experiencing at any given time. However, symptoms can and very often do change as an eating disorder evolves. A person's body weight can fluctuate either up or down. These things do not inform us about the severity of their psychopathology, which can remain significant despite a weight increase or evolving symptoms. Neither do they reflect the impact of the eating disorder on the person's overall physical health or the detriment it is having on their wider life.

Squeezing people into the existing diagnostic labels and moving them to new categories as their presentation changes makes the assessment and diagnosis of eating disorders more complicated than it needs to be. It also removes the focus from what matters. While the current categories exist, vital research studies are excluding large numbers of people with eating disorders just because they don't tick the right diagnostic boxes. Treatment offered to people is also adjusted depending on the eating disorder classification they have been given.

As I detail in the coming chapters, it's my belief that restrictive eating disorders are a brain-based addiction to an internal state of energy deficit—irrespective of weight or the reasons the person's brain uses to rationalise their powerfully compulsive and destructive behaviours. Treatment and research for restrictive eating disorders needs to be inclusive to everyone affected.

---

1. Stice E, Marti CN, Rohde P. Prevalence, incidence, impairment, and course of the proposed DSM-5 eating disorder diagnoses in an 8-year prospective community study of young women. J Abnorm Psychol. 2013 May; 122(2):445-57. doi: 10.1037/a0030679. Epub 2012 Nov 12. PMID: 23148784; PMCID: PMC3980846.

2. Neville H. Golden, Philip S. Mehler. Atypical anorexia nervosa can be just as bad. Cleveland Clinic Journal of Medicine. Mar 2020, 87 (3) 172-174; doi: 10.3949/ccjm.87a.19146.

3. Harrop EN, Mensinger JL, Moore M, Lindhorst T. Restrictive eating disorders in higher weight persons: A systematic review of atypical anorexia nervosa prevalence and consecutive admission literature. Int J Eat Disord. 2021 Aug; 54(8):1328-1357. doi: 10.1002/eat.23519. Epub 2021 Apr 17. PMID: 33864277; PMCID: PMC9035356.

4. Koomar T, Thomas TR, Pottschmidt NR, Lutter M, and Michaelson JJ. (2021) Estimating the prevalence and genetic risk mechanisms of ARFID in a large autism cohort. Front. Psychiatry 12:668297. doi: 10.3389/fpsyt.2021.668297.

5. Berrettini W. The genetics of eating disorders. Psychiatry (Edgmont). 2004 Nov; 1(3): 18–25. PMID: 21191522; PMCID: PMC3010958.

# Chapter Two

---

# Addictions & Eating Disorders Compared

T his chapter provides an initial overview of what addictions are and how eating disorders compare, before exploring the neuroscience driving them.

An addiction generally starts when someone either consumes an addictive substance (such as drugs or alcohol) or engages in a habit-forming behaviour that makes them feel great. Their brain's reward system creates a large pleasure response which drives them to want to repeat the same experience. For a while, the substance or behaviour continues to make them feel good and creates immense internal rewards. However, over time, the person's brain produces a rise in their anxiety and emotion response circuits, which go into overdrive when they are not engaging in the addiction. This resulting agitative state compels

the person to continue to pursue their *drug*, no longer for pleasure, but to escape how highly anxious or depressed they feel if
they don't.

Compare this now to an eating disorder. If you have a restrictive eating disorder, it's likely that when you first engaged
in behaviours that created an energy deficit, you felt good. Examples of these are restrictive eating, exercise or other purging
behaviours. The behaviours in themselves might have given
you feelings of pleasure or even *highs*. In addition to this, the
rewards gained as a result of praise from others for some initial
weight loss or a self-satisfaction at seeing the numbers on the
scales go down added to a sense of achievement and positive
feeling. This resulted in your brain seeking out more of what led
to this internal sense of reward. However, as the eating disorder
took hold, you stopped getting the same buzz from engaging in
the behaviours. Despite this, you felt seemingly powerless to stop
them because attempting to do so led to agitation, anxiety or
even panic and low mood. Your brain quickly learnt that the
agitation and anxiety at not engaging in the behaviours were
instantly overcome by continuing to pursue them. This has now
become so efficient that the behaviours are now automatic before you consciously begin to sense any discomfort. In this way,
the automatic pursuit of these now compulsive behaviours gives
you an ongoing sense of calm and an ability to feel somewhat
*normal.*

• • • ● • ● ● • ●

# Typical Signs of Addiction and Restrictive Eating Disorders

Perhaps the biggest indication that someone has developed an addiction is when they continue to pursue their *drug** despite clear evidence that it has a detrimental impact on their life. These negative consequences might be on their work and studies, relationships or physical and mental health. Very often, all these aspects are affected.

If you have a restrictive eating disorder, behaviours that lead to an internal state of energy deficit—such as restrictive eating, exercise or other forms of purging—can quickly become compulsive and addictive.

The following signs are typically present in an addiction. For each of these signs, a comparison is made to the experience of an eating disorder:

## TOLERANCE

A need to engage in an increasing level of the *drug* to feel the same positive effects. With an eating disorder, many people find that the level of restrictive eating or amount of exercise they engage in increases over time. If you have one or two days of increased restriction or exercise, you can find it incredibly hard to reduce it back to the level it was previously. This is because the feel-good or numbing effects from the behaviours are now linked to that higher level of engagement.

## COPING MECHANISM

Over time the *drug* becomes a way to cope with emotions and to feel normal to the extent that you develop a dependence on it. People with eating disorders quickly begin to use the behaviours to manage difficult emotions or stress. When this incredibly effective coping mechanism is not available, levels of distress can build quickly.

## WITHDRAWAL

If someone is unable to pursue their usual *drug* fix, they are likely to feel anxious, irritable, restless and/or depressed, and they might experience sleep problems. If you are attempting to overcome an eating disorder, you will very likely experience these *withdrawal* symptoms when you stop engaging in the disordered behaviours. These symptoms can also occur when an external factor prevents you from engaging in your habitual compulsions.

## LACK OF CONTROL OVER THE DRUG

This is reflected in unsuccessful attempts to cut back on or stop engaging altogether with the *drug* despite wanting to. Perhaps you have tried to stop exercising to overcome the eating disorder but within an hour found yourself pounding the streets before you realised what had happened. Or maybe you can relate to situations such as saying to yourself, *Today I will eat a brownie with my lunch,* only to find that the discomfort became overpowering, and you resorted to your usual low-fat yoghurt instead.

## TIME

The *drug* consumes a huge amount of time, from planning for the behaviour, engaging in it or recovering from it. Many people with eating disorders spend a lot of time engaging in habitual lower-level movement and more formal exercise. Time is also commonly taken up on planning out restrictive food intake and consumed by engaging in ritualistic eating behaviours which in themselves are compulsive.

## REDUCTION OR NEGLECT OF OTHER AREAS OF LIFE

The increasing engagement and preoccupation with the *drug* leaves other life activities and relationships neglected, even those you consider to be of high value. Perhaps you stopped engaging socially, neglected relationships or allowed your career choices to be impacted so that you could devote more attention to the pursuit of the disordered behaviours.

## CONTINUING THE DRUG DESPITE NEGATIVE LIFE CONSEQUENCES

Eating disorder behaviours cause physical, psychological, social and interpersonal problems, and yet even when you can recognise this, it can be incredibly hard to stop. It is likely that you continue to eat restrictive amounts despite clear indications from your body or even warnings from health professionals that continuing to do so could lead to significant physical harm. If compulsive exercise is part of the eating disorder, it's possible that you have continued to exercise despite illness or injury.

## MINIMISING THE EXTENT OF THE PROBLEM

This can be hiding how great an impact your dependence on the *drug* has or how often you are engaging in the behaviours. Perhaps you have attempted to reassure your family or friends that you are eating sufficiently by leading them to believe you are eating more than you are. You might have experienced self-denial in relation to physical symptoms caused by the eating disorder. Maybe you have attempted to reassure yourself or others that the behaviours you engage in are *healthy choices*.

Comparing the typical signs of an addiction to those of an eating disorder clearly highlights the strong parallels in both their manifestation and the impact they have on a person's life.

An addiction, which an eating disorder is arguably a form of, can take a huge toll on a person's life, relationships, general functioning and finances. The addiction becomes increasingly disabling and distressing, especially when they want to stop but find themselves seemingly incapable of doing so.

*The term drug is used throughout the book to refer to any addictive drug, whether that is an actual ingested substance, a behaviour or the internal state of energy deficit*

• • • ●•● ●• •

# Restrictive Eating Disorders as an Addiction to Energy Deficit

The concept of this book is based on the compelling theory that restrictive eating disorders are an addiction to the body being in a state of energy deficit.

For most people, being in a state of energy deficit is unpleasant. They will get hungry, become irritable, shaky and depressed. Yet people with restrictive eating disorders appear to get a calming and anxiolytic effect from it. To people with restrictive eating disorders, energy deficit seems to have similar effects as those experienced by people addicted to other forms of *drugs*.

### What Is Energy Deficit?

Energy deficit is a physiological state in which your body has insufficient energy in terms of energy coming in and/or stored energy supplies to meet its requirements. There are more details on this in Chapter 10, but it is important to be aware that an energy deficit is not only related to insufficient calories being consumed relative to those being used. Energy deficit also relates to whether your body has sufficient fat and lean tissue stores to meet the minimally necessary level that your brain recognises it needs. If your body is below this minimum level, you will remain in a state of energy deficit until your body mass is restored and until you are consistently consuming sufficient energy (or calories) to meet your body's ongoing demands. Please note that the necessary level in relation to your body composition is largely genetically determined and cannot be predicted by a doctor or a BMI chart.

When the *drug* you are addicted to is a physiological state, as is the case with a restrictive eating disorder, it is less easy to identify as an addiction, and it is harder to pinpoint which aspects of your life and behaviours relate to it. This is especially true when comparing eating disorders as a form of addiction to someone who has an addiction to drugs, gambling or pornography, which are much easier to identify as such. This is very likely why eating disorders have yet to be widely recognised as a form of addiction.

### How Does an Addiction to Energy Deficit Develop?

When you developed an eating disorder, you initially engaged in behaviours that put your body into a state of energy deficit. Your brain received a high reward response from this physiological state, which was very possibly reinforced by praise from those around you for the weight you had lost. This reward response will have generated high feelings of pleasure and a drive to repeat the behaviours that created this feeling. Any behaviours that you engaged in to create a deeper energy deficit were rewarded by your brain, using a chemical called dopamine, which reinforced them and gave them a highly addictive quality. Over a short space of time, these behaviours will have become compulsive and hard to stop, even as your reward response from them decreased.

## Behaviours Within a Restrictive Eating Disorder That Can Become Addictive

When you have a restrictive eating disorder, there are two categories of behaviours that can become addictive or compulsive.

The first category includes behaviours that directly lead to energy deficit and either maintain or deepen it. These are instantly rewarding because they are related to the instant pursuit of the energy deficit state, which is ultimately the *drug fix* that your brain is seeking.

The second category includes behaviours that arise as a direct result of your being in a semi-starved or energy deficit state. Chapter 9 provides more information on starvation syndrome and the common effects to being in a semi-starved state. For someone with an eating disorder, these starvation behaviours can also become deeply ingrained, hard-to-break habits and they entwine in the same brain networks driving the first category of behaviours.

There are a significant number of addictive behaviours that you can develop with a restrictive eating disorder. The behaviours you are affected by will also differ to those of someone else. Some of these behaviours will be insidious and can be hidden behind those which are more obviously *disordered*. To overcome the eating disorder, you will need to address all your learned compulsive and addictive behaviours so that your brain can fully reprogram.

Listed below are some of the most common addictive and compulsive behaviours seen in someone with a restrictive eating disorder. As stated above, everyone experiences a different *cocktail* of these. This *cocktail* can also change over time as the eating disorder evolves, because the overarching addiction is to energy deficit, and so the reward comes from any behaviours that create this internal state. Over time, one set of behaviours in pursuit of energy deficit might stop creating such a powerful effect or become harder to sustain. This leaves you seeking an alternative behaviour for the same energy deficit *fix*.

### Addictive and Compulsive Behaviours Common to Restrictive Eating Disorders

### Behaviours That Directly Create Energy Deficit:

- Food restriction in any form, which might be restricting amounts, macros, micros, avoiding certain food types or only making *healthy choices*

- Exercise and movement, including lower-level movement, such as constantly standing, fidgeting, doing housework or keeping busy

- Purging through vomiting

- Using laxatives or diet pills

- Weighing and measuring foods (to restrict)

- Calorie or other macro counting

- Using apps or Fitbit-type devices to track food intake, movement, heart rate, weight or anything else

- Chewing and spitting

- Feeling addicted to the sensation of an *empty* stomach

- Weighing yourself or body checking

**Behaviours That Arise from Starvation Syndrome:**

- Visiting supermarkets or other food stores (even though nothing is bought)

- Looking at recipes or obsessing over food in other ways, such as scrolling through *food porn* images on social media

- A strong compulsion to restrict on money spending

- Hoarding or collecting items, food related or otherwise

Chapter 5 covers the issue of multiple addictions and the impact this can have when you are attempting to overcome a restrictive eating disorder.

*I have deliberately left binge eating off these lists. Although binge eating in someone with a restrictive eating disorder can have addictive properties, I would not consider them within the same category of addictive behaviours underlying the restrictive eating disorder. There is more information on binge eating and how to address it in Chapter 4.*

•••••••••••

# The Addiction Model and Other Theories for Eating Disorders

The following chapters explore the addiction model for restrictive eating disorders in more detail. But before moving on, I want to reassure you that the addiction model fits comfortably alongside other theories for eating disorders that you might be familiar with.

There are, of course, many theories as to what eating disorders are and their causes. Most of these are largely speculative. One thing we do know about eating disorders is that there's still so much to learn in order to really understand them. Sadly, there are still theories today that are based on outdated psychological models, which are not explored here. I do, though, refer to some of the more credible theories that are often cited in eating disorder communities today. By demonstrating how the addiction model fits within these, I hope to take your understanding of eating disorders to a new level.

Each of the below theories of eating disorders is discussed in much more detail later in the book. This introductory overview is to help you understand where the addiction model sits within these other theories and provide context for the information provided in the next chapters.

## The *Fear of Weight Gain* Theory

In recent years within the eating disorder community, one phrase has been used more than any other, which is that eating disorders are a *fear of weight gain*. I hold my hands up, I've said it, and to some extent it's a statement with some validity in today's culture. However, I've always had a niggling discomfort with the *fear of weight gain* theory as an explanation for eating disorders. Yes, in our modern society where there is a thin ideal, many people with eating disorders do have a *fear* of weight gain or a strong discomfort at the thought of gaining weight. BUT this is not true for all. When you look to the cases of restrictive eating disorders through history, in times that preceded diet culture, none of those affected would have attributed a fear of weight gain to be the cause of their self-starvation behaviours. This is why I was led to reflect more deeply on what eating disorders really are and to speculate that, rather than eating disorders stemming from a fear of weight gain, they are in fact a powerful addiction to energy deficit. Someone with a restrictive eating disorder in today's culture might fear weight gain but this fear alone does not push them to the extreme ability to semi-starve themselves in the alluring, yet destructive ways commonly seen.

## The Evolutionary Flee-from-Famine Theory

The flee-from-famine theory to eating disorders speculates that restrictive eating disorders developed as a useful evolution-ary response to a famine situation[1]. This theory offers immense credibility, and it sits well alongside the addiction model. When our ancestors needed to flee from a famine situation, it would have been beneficial if their brains could change so that they were disinclined to stop and eat the few resources they had where they were and instead move to find an environment of food abundance. For them to be able to defy their current hunger and keep moving was life-saving. However, it would not have been possible without a sense of internal reward at doing so that was greater than the immediate rewards they gained from eating in the moment. Therefore, within this theory, a person's brain becoming *addicted* to restricting food intake, constant movement and not wasting other available resources fits with it being an evolutionary survival response.

### Energy Deficit Triggers the Onset of an Eating Disorder

The theory that energy deficit is a key factor in triggering the onset of a restrictive eating disorder[2] is also supported in the addiction model. If restrictive eating disorders are understood to be an addiction to energy deficit, it makes sense that energy deficit is a requirement to their onset.

### The Genetic Evidence to Eating Disorders

The addiction model to eating disorders also sits alongside the evolving genetic evidence supporting the theory that there is a genetic contribution to the development of eating disorders[3]. Addictions to other substances or behaviours are also thought to have a genetic link, and the addiction model to an eating disorder is very compatible with the genetic evidence.

In summary, the theory that eating disorders are a form of addiction does not invalidate existing theories of eating disorders. In fact, the addiction model adds further context to these other, often widely cited and accepted theories to eating disorders.

---

1. Guisinger S. Adapted to flee famine: adding an evolutionary perspective on anorexia nervosa. Psychol Rev. 2003 Oct; 110(4):745-61. doi: 10.1037/0033-295X.110.4.745. PMID: 14599241.

2. Scharner S, Stengel A. Animal models for anorexia nervosa—a systematic review. Front Hum Neurosci. 2021 Jan 20;14:596381. doi: 10.3389/fnhum.2020.596381. PMID: 33551774; PMCID: PMC7854692.

3. Watson, HJ, Yilmaz, Z, Thornton, LM, et al. Genome-wide association study identifies eight risk loci and implicates metabo-psychiatric origins for anorexia nervosa. Nat Genet 51, 1207-1214 (2019). https://doi.org/10.1038/s41588-019-0439-2.

# Chapter Three

---

# Neuroscience of the Addiction Model for Eating Disorders

## Basic Neuroscience of Learning, Habits & Addictions

Let's now explore some basic neuroscience in relation to what's happening in the brain on a structural and chemical level when someone develops an addiction to anything. This might be a substance, a behaviour or, as with a restrictive eating disorder, the internal state of energy deficit.

The brain is incredibly complicated. It is a sophisticated and intelligent organ. Even with all the research and science we have today, exactly how the brain works and all the amazing things it does remains beyond the understanding of any neuroscientist.

Of course, that's not to say that we don't know anything about the brain and how it works. Experts are learning more every day. This section covers a simple explanation of what is known to be happening inside the brain when someone develops any new learning or habits and when these turn into an addiction. This information is provided to help you to understand what has occurred in your brain as you developed a restrictive eating disorder (as a form of addiction) and, from this, begin to understand what's necessary to overcome it.

### A Simple Introduction to the Brain

The human brain is made up of billions of cells called neurons. These neurons organise themselves into a huge mesh of circuits and networks. Different circuits and networks are responsible for driving different functions, actions and behaviours. Neurons connect to other neurons within their circuits via connections called synapses, which are small gaps between the cells. The first neuron in the circuit will communicate with the next by releasing a chemical, known as a neurotransmitter, into the synapse, where it crosses to the next neuron. A key neurotransmitter in the development and maintenance of addictions is dopamine. This is something you will become very familiar with if you keep reading!

There are a couple of key brain regions to know about when considering habits and addictions. These are:

- The basal ganglia and the striatum which sits within it. This is located at the base of the forebrain. The function of the striatum is to push us to pursue our goals and feel the pleasurable effects from them. In terms of survival through evolution, this was essential for goals such as finding food and shelter, sex (necessary for procreation) and ensuring our overall safety. This part of the brain is also key in the formation of habits and is a significant part of the brain's reward circuit.

- The prefrontal cortex (PFC) is located at the front of the brain, just behind the forehead. The dorsolateral PFC is responsible for our judgments, decision-making and insight, and it's generally considered the centre of our *executive* function. The PFC is key in impulse control and determining whether a behaviour is a good idea before pursuing it. It is a change in the circuitry between the PFC and the striatum that is key in addictions. The inhibitory control that would usually arise from the PFC if a behaviour or action is considered unwise is markedly reduced, which leaves the person much more likely to continue to pursue the addictive behaviour in a compulsive way as they are less able to consider the consequences.

## What Are Habits and How Do They Develop?

Before going deeper into what's happening in the brain when someone has developed an addiction, it's worth clarifying what habits are on a brain-based level.

A definition of a habit is:
*Behaviours that have become so ingrained that we perform them automatically and autonomously of the outcome.*[1]
In extreme forms, habits can become compulsions and addictions.

Compulsive behaviours occur without the need of conscious thought processing. They are automatic and triggered by cues. Habits are referred to here as behaviours, but they can also be thoughts and emotions.

Habitual behaviour differs from purposeful behaviour. When a behaviour is purposeful, it will stop if the outcome is no longer required. With habitual behaviour, on the other hand, the consequences of the behaviours are no longer considered, and the behaviours will persist even if they are no longer wanted. Habits ultimately become driven (or triggered), not by their outcome, but by environmental cues or emotional states. Habitual behaviours are linked to past experiences and are a form of embedded learning. They are also characterised by their inflexibility.

As stated above, it is within the striatum (in the basal ganglia) that new learning and behaviours can form into habits.

If we repeat a behaviour in pursuit of our goals, and this behaviour is rewarding—usually due to the release of the body's
natural opiates, such as endorphins, alongside a higher release
of dopamine—then learning of this behaviour will occur at a
deep brain level within the striatum. Over time it will become
*wired in* as a habit. When a highly rewarding and newly learnt
behaviour develops into a habit, its processing shifts from one
section of the striatum to another as it becomes even more
deeply embedded.

Once the new habit is fully embedded into the brain's circuitry, the brain will *chunk* in the new activity, as this requires
even less mental energy and can occur on autopilot. Chunking
is when the brain will convert a sequence of actions into an
automatic routine. By chunking in as many habits as possible,
the brain has more space to focus on other things.

Ultimately, we consider something to have become a habit
when it occurs automatically and is triggered by specific events
or contexts. When we first develop habits, they are frequently based on reward-based learning (from endogenous opiates
and dopamine), which after enough experience and repetition
require less and less reward. Learning that becomes habitual
is performed automatically. These behaviours also develop a
resilience to competing actions that might lead to unlearning
of this habitual pathway. This helps to explain why, with an
eating disorder, you still find yourself automatically engaged in
disordered, habitual behaviours, even though they no longer give
you any sense of reward and you might have even grown to hate
them.

## What About Dopamine?

Dopamine is a key neurotransmitter that is released in pursuit of a goal, promoting motivation towards it. When the goal is achieved, a greater surge of dopamine is released, creating feelings of pleasure and reward. From an evolutionary perspective, these goals would have been related to the things that were essential for survival, such as socialising, sex, eating or feeling warm and comfortable.

When our brain recognises pleasure from an experience, it's more likely to pursue it again. The dopamine released into the striatum as a result of a pleasurable experience makes the brain pay attention and signals to it that this experience is worth repeating. Dopamine also promotes the necessary changes in the brain circuitry that ensure it is much easier to follow this pleasurable pathway again. Therefore, these behaviours can quickly form into habits.

When a person develops an addiction, they experience a much greater surge in dopamine from engagement in the addictive *drug* than that experienced from other behaviours. This wave of pleasure results in their brain recognising what caused this dopamine release and labelling it as worthy of repetition. The dopamine surge also creates connections in their brain between the addictive *drug,* feelings of high pleasure and any external cues that were present at the time of *drug* engagement. This results in the person developing brain circuitry that pushes them to pursue this rewarding *drug* over and above other goals and activities in their life.

With an addiction, because the *drug* creates a surge in dopamine beyond that experienced from more moderately rewarding activities, the brain adapts to the higher dopamine levels by reducing the number of receptors in the neurons that can receive dopamine signals. Therefore, the person experiences much less pleasure from activities that they used to enjoy. At the same time, they require increasing levels of engagement in their *drug* to experience even a moderate level of pleasure or reward from it.

Following a dopamine surge, the brain attempts to bring dopamine levels back to a baseline level, by dropping the levels below baseline to what is considered a deficit state. This makes a person feel depressed, anxious and agitated, wanting to pursue the *hit* created by the addiction again. This dopamine seesaw effect that drives addictions is explained in more detail later in this chapter.

Over time, people with addictions become flat and depressed and have much less motivation to do things that others consider pleasurable. This is why they have a need for increasing levels of their *drug* to experience just normal levels of reward and a calmer state.

**Bringing It All Together...**

The striatum and the PFC usually communicate well together. The striatum pushes us towards a goal and focused on achieving it. The PFC applies rational reasoning to the goal pursuit so that it can be achieved safely and optimally, inhibiting any behaviours that might be judged to be too risky or unwise.

Dopamine activates these systems. It helps to narrow our focus and attention on the goal, while driving desire (motivation). Dopamine is released as we pursue the goal and is responsible in the pleasure and sense of reward gained from achieving it.

When a person develops an addiction, there is a breakdown in the communication between the PFC and the striatum when the addictive *drug* is on the horizon. It might be said that when a person is in pursuit of their *drug*, their PFC goes offline. This results in their pursuing the *drug* even when doing so has become damaging, because they are less able to apply reason or logic when in pursuit of it. In addition to this, the levels of dopamine in an addicted person's brain become destabilised.

The brain lays down new neural circuits and networks when it develops new habits, by forming bonds between the neurons in those circuits and making them stronger. However, at the same time, the synapses and bonds between neurons in circuits that are no longer being used are considered unneeded by the brain. The brain *prunes* or thins these out to become more streamlined at achieving its goals, ensuring it can pursue them with greater efficiency and speed. As a sleek machine, the brain seeks to lay down fast and efficient pathways that it can follow easily and habitually; it then takes less future effort to follow those habits and frees up space for other conscious thoughts and processing. This is a positive process in forming the habits we want but not helpful when it comes to the development of addictive habits.

• • • ● • ● • • •

# The Deep Learning Model of Addiction

Are addictions a form of disease in which the person with the addiction has a brain that is somehow altered? There are certainly experts who will argue that addictions are a chronic form of disease and that they should be treated as such, labelled as an illness and medicalised.

However, there are also a growing number of addiction experts who now argue that addictions are not pathological and should not be considered a disease. They state that the brain changes seen in an addiction are no different to those seen when a person develops other strong habits.

One of these addiction experts is a neuroscientist, Dr Marc Lewis. He is now a professor of neuroscience, but he had an addiction to heroin, cocaine and other substances between the ages of eighteen and thirty. Dr Lewis maintains that addictions, of which he considers eating disorders to be one, are not incurable *diseases* that at best can only be managed through abstinence for life, but that they are a form of *deep learning*[2]. I agree with his perspective, and by considering eating disorders as a form of addiction, it led me to also understand them to be a form of *deep learning*. When you understand eating disorders in this way, you can appreciate how overcoming them, although challenging, is possible and that people with eating disorders should not be made to feel otherwise.

## Deep Learning

The deep learning model of addiction states that engagement in an addictive *drug* creates an increase in the dopamine system within the striatum that pushes the person to pursue the *drug* with strong feelings of desire and motivation. This is coupled with changes in the brain areas responsible for judgment and decision-making (the PFC), resulting in significant changes in the brain's circuitry.

Within the PFC, insight, decision-making and judgment are usually applied to goals to ensure they are achieved safely and optimally. A strong brain circuit exists between the PFC and striatum to ensure the two brain regions talk to one another and drive behaviours. In someone with an addiction, this communication in relation to the addictive *drug* between the PFC and striatum breaks down as the behaviours become automatic and ingrained. This results in the person losing perspective on the reality of their actions whenever their *drug* is on the horizon. They ultimately become much less capable of considering their own sense of future or whether pursuing the *drug* in that moment is worth it.

The constant pursuit of the *drug* that stimulates the reward system (dopamine) leaves someone only able to think about the here and now in terms of obtaining that *reward* and much less capable of understanding or considering longer term consequences. Things that used to be attractive, such as family, social situations or old hobbies, fall away to the point that with time, the synapses in their brain relating to pursuit of those things are pruned out because they are not being used.

Some argue that imagery taken of the brains of *addicts* show that their PFC is thinner than in *normal* people and so they have brain changes that reflect disease. However, Dr Lewis argues that this reflects a brain that has become more streamlined at pursuing its goals. The brain will thin out or prune weakened synapses in unneeded pathways as a normal and healthy response to consolidate learning. He argues that these same brain changes can occur from a huge range of behaviours that pursue something highly attractive and rewarding. It is the nature of the pursuit that has resulted in some being classified a *disease* by medical practitioners (such as drugs, alcohol and eating disorders) and yet others are seen as acceptable, even applauded (such as the pursuit of money or falling in love!).

The good news is that there is strong research evidence to the theory that addictive and deeply learnt habits can be overcome, enabling the person impacted to replace old habits with new ones. The brain can *unlearn* old behaviours and develop new brain networks driving healthier pursuits.

The other positive point is that once someone consciously decides to pursue new behaviours to form new pathways and habits, if those pathways have been used in the past (for example, before the addictive disorder developed), then the brain is very likely to still have some wiring for it, which it can pick up again and follow with more ease each time.

Additionally, when someone stops pursuing their addiction and finds new goals to pursue, the brain thinning seen in the PFC increases in volume again and does so to a point of crossing a baseline when compared to those who never had an addiction. This implies the brain can recover in full, and people can learn new behaviours and habits that can further promote the decline of old networks used during the addiction. Therefore, the brain changes seen in addiction are not chronic, pruned synapses can be replaced, and the brain can rewire and heal.

## Applying the Deep Learning Model to Eating Disorders

If you have an eating disorder, then the deep learning model should offer you hope and allow you to trust that overcoming an eating disorder is possible. The *deep learning* your brain has undertaken with the eating disorder, which drives the compulsive and habitual eating disorder behaviours, is powerful. However, there is nothing fundamentally different in the way your brain works compared to the workings of any brain that has learnt to pursue something that was initially very attractive and rewarding. Studies are showing that when a person does overcome an eating disorder, their brain function is the same as someone who never had an eating disorder at all[3]. This should reassure you that even after years or decades of an eating disorder, the brain can return to function normally.

When you stop pursuing the habitual eating disordered behaviours and pursue the goals of eating without restriction and avoiding any means of compensation, your brain can and will create new neuronal networks, and over time the old circuits driving the pursuit of energy deficit will decline. This concept is commonly referred to in eating disorder circles as *rewiring*.

•••••••••

# The Dopamine Balance Model of Addiction

In addition to being a form of deep learning, addictions are also understood to be a change in the brain's dopamine balance, which drives the pursuit of a behaviour or substance, even when the *drug* being pursued no longer brings pleasure.

Understanding more about what is happening to the brain's dopamine balance in someone with an addiction can help you to understand why addictive disorders (including eating disorders) are so pervasive and difficult to overcome.

As discussed earlier, dopamine is a key chemical involved in motivation and the experience of pleasure and reward. The more dopamine that is released in response to a substance or behaviour—and the faster it is released—the higher the likelihood that it will lead to an addiction. A person with a restrictive eating disorder likely experienced a high surge in dopamine release when they initially engaged in restriction, exercise or other behaviours that created a significant enough state of energy deficit. This dopamine surge quickly led to the addictive nature of the disorder.

### The Dopamine Balance

Dopamine is released in everyone's brain to maintain a level baseline at all times. This baseline is called homeostasis.

The brain becomes sensitive to this homeostatic point, and any change from this level gives the brain important information. An increase in dopamine feels pleasurable. In this way, it is reinforcing to the brain and leads to an urge to pursue whatever caused the increase. A drop in dopamine from baseline creates feelings that are unpleasant, such as anxiety or low mood. This change in how we feel tells the brain to push us to change our current circumstances and find ways to seek more dopamine.

To explain the dopamine system better, a psychiatrist and addiction expert, Dr Anna Lembke, describes dopamine in the brain as being on a *seesaw* or a balance[4].

If the balance tips in one direction, we experience pleasure, and if it tips the other way, we experience pain. Ultimately, the brain wants to keep the balance level and will do what it can to maintain homeostasis.

When the balance on the pleasure-pain dopamine seesaw tips to the pleasure side, the brain will attempt to re-establish balance by reducing dopamine release and transmission. BUT—and this is a crucial thing to understand—instead of just returning the dopamine level to baseline so that it is at a stable balance again, the brain will first drop dopamine levels below baseline. This below-baseline drop in dopamine after a pleasurable experience creates the sensation of coming down after a high and feelings of emotional pain. These feelings will quickly create an urge or desire to repeat the behaviour to get dopamine levels back up. If you wait long enough, the dopamine levels will return to normal of their own accord. However, it's this seesaw dopamine effect that drives people to continue to pursue rewarding behaviours, not just for the rewards they bring but because not doing so becomes uncomfortable.

When thinking about dopamine using the seesaw analogy, it's key to remember that what goes up will eventually come down to the same degree of change from baseline.

If someone continues to bombard their reward system with more and more dopamine by continuing to pursue dopamine-releasing behaviours, the pleasure side on the dopamine seesaw will go ever higher. However, this also means that the pain side of the dopamine seesaw is becoming more heavily weighted down when the behaviour is not being pursued. Over time, this results in the need to engage in ever-increasing dopamine-releasing behaviours to just feel *normal*. This is why people with addictions need to engage in their *drug* at higher levels, in different forms or with more intensity to simply experience a feeling of normality, let alone pleasure.

### An Addicted Brain & the Dopamine Balance

An addicted brain is one where the pain side of the pleasure-pain dopamine balance has become excessively tilted to the pain side because of the ongoing pursuit of the addictive *drug*. This is also referred to as being in a dopamine deficit state.

The chase of dopamine alters what is termed the *hedonic set point* in the brain, so the ability to feel any form of joy is very hard to reach. People ultimately become *anhedonic*, which literally means unable to feel pleasure. At this point people become incapable of experiencing joy or pleasure from experiences that would usually have been pleasurable. Someone with an addiction therefore develops a reduced ability to enjoy pleasure from pursuing their *drug* or from any other usually pleasurable pursuits in life, and they have a much higher state of inner pain.

With a chronically tilted dopamine seesaw to the pain side, someone with an addictive disorder will be walking around with a sense of inner pain whenever they are not *using*. They will also need to engage in higher levels or more intense forms of the *drug*, not for reward but just to feel *normal*. Their ability to feel any pleasure at what can be considered normal rewards will have diminished.

At this point, whenever the person is not engaging in their *drug*, they will experience all the common symptoms of withdrawal, such as agitation, anxiety, irritability, insomnia, depression and intrusive thoughts of needing to use. These symptoms can also be described as *cravings*, which drive them back to the *drug* because the dopamine deficit created whenever they are not engaging in it results in excruciating inner pain.

### Applying the Dopamine Balance Model to Eating Disorders

When you have a restrictive eating disorder, you will be in a chronic dopamine deficit state. This means the dopamine balance in your brain is severely tilted to the side of pain whenever you are not engaged in the pursuit of your *drug*, i.e., energy deficit.

When you first developed the eating disorder, engaging in the behaviours that created energy deficit—such as restriction, exercise, purging or other compensatory methods—felt good. In fact, the initial surge in dopamine from your level baseline point probably made you feel amazing. When you were not engaging in those behaviours, your dopamine initially just tipped below baseline, making you feel a little uncomfortable and giving you a push to pursue them again. As this cycle went on and you engaged in increasing levels of behaviours that pushed your dopamine *seesaw* to the pleasure side, the pain side of the dopamine balance in your brain was becoming more heavily weighted down. This means that now, whenever you are not engaging in the disordered behaviours, you feel anxious, depressed and agitated.

Over time, the disordered behaviours very likely lost a lot of their pleasurable effects, but now you continue to engage in them because not doing so leaves you in intense internal pain, with anxiety and low mood. On the flip side, pursuing the eating disorder behaviours is the only way to bring your dopamine balance back to a point that allows you to feel some sense of inner calm or numbness. Because your hedonic set point is now also altered, you have probably lost your ability to experience enjoyment from other things in life that were once pleasurable to you.

Many people attempting to overcome an eating disorder argue that exercise is the only thing that helps their anxiety. This is not because they are experiencing the mental health benefits of exercise that someone without an addiction to it can experience. Someone with an eating disorder experiences a calming effect from exercise because it is restoring their dopamine balance temporarily to a more baseline level. However, at the same time, it is also creating an even greater dip effect on the pain side. Therefore, continuing to engage with this behaviour will merely lead to higher levels of agitation, anxiety and depression in the longer term and a need to keep exercising more to continue to feel any sense of normal.

### Restoring Dopamine Balance

You might be reading this and thinking, *Okay, so the last section said that the brain can heal from the changes in wiring that have occurred from an addictive disorder, but what about this dopamine imbalance? Does the fact that my brain currently has a chronic dopamine deficit leave me destined to a life of eating disordered behaviours just to feel anything other than depressed and anxious?*

Happily, the answer is that you *can* restore the dopamine levels in your brain to a stable balance. The bad news is that as you go through this process, you will have to tolerate a period of feeling the effects of the dopamine deficit, which as described above can include feelings of anxiety, depression and agitation.

If you do stop the pursuit of energy deficit and all the behaviours that lead to or maintain this, your dopamine levels will initially drop to the deficit state they are currently in. This will feel horrible, but if you continue to abstain and not push on the pleasure side of the seesaw by going back to restriction or compensatory behaviours, then your brain will slowly and naturally restore your baseline dopamine level to the point of equilibrium. When this happens, you will feel calm and stable and get the sense that the *real you* is returning without needing to use the eating disorder behaviours to achieve this. You will also find yourself able to experience pleasure from the small things in life again. This is referred to as a *dopamine reset.*

The best way to achieve a dopamine reset is to abstain from the addictive *drug* long enough to allow dopamine levels to completely restore and rebalance. It perhaps goes without saying that this is much easier said than done, as this initial period of abstinence, creating a vast dopamine deficit, is going to be very painful. People who do go through it need to be prepared for some very challenging emotions, as well as mental and physical symptoms.

The dopamine model of addiction also supports the argument that addictions are not arising from a brain that is *abnormal* or *diseased*. Dr Lembke believes that any person's brain can develop this dopamine imbalance, resulting in an addiction if they pursue a pleasurable reward to a high enough degree. Any brain has the potential for addiction, but other factors, such as genetics or social and cultural factors, can make one person more likely to develop an addiction in the form of an eating disorder and another become addicted to gambling or drugs. For both models of addiction, the changes that occur can return to a balanced state.

• • • ●•● • • ·

# Combining the Deep Learning & Dopamine Balance Models of Addiction

It helps to combine the dopamine and deep learning models to understand addictions more comprehensively and, in this way, eating disorders too from a brain-based perspective. In doing so, you can understand why an eating disorder is so powerful and hard to overcome. There are two key brain processes driving the compulsive habits you have developed in order to pursue your *drug* of energy deficit.

Firstly, your brain has developed hardwired and deeply in-grained habitual pathways to pursue energy deficit. Your PFC goes *offline* when it comes to this pursuit and all the associated behaviours. Therefore, you are following these behaviours habitually, and you are less able to apply rational thought or impulse control to stop yourself from doing so.

Secondly, you have a dopamine balance that over time has developed a significant deficit from the ongoing pursuit of the originally *pleasurable* rewards that these behaviours gave you. This means that now not pursuing your usual *hit* of energy deficit results in intense feelings of pain. These withdrawal symptoms and cravings are so strong that they push your brain automatically back down the deeply embedded habitual circuits that are driving the ongoing pursuit of energy deficit, to immediately numb the pain. This all happens without it entering your conscious awareness.

## Can Eating Disorders *Really* Be Considered a Form of Addiction?

While you were reading the previous sections about models for addiction and their application to eating disorders, you might have been thinking that this is all speculation without much evidence to support it.

Although there isn't a huge volume of research evidence available that has pursued the addiction theory of eating disorders and studied the brain in relation to this, there is some. There's also a body of professionals currently fighting for eating disorders to be formally reclassified as a form of addiction. At present, they are particularly pushing for bulimia nervosa (BN) to be categorised as an addictive disorder. This is because it's recognised that purging through vomiting causes a release of natural endorphins, providing a person with even greater numbing effects and adding to the addictive potential of the behaviour. It could be argued that the same can be said for other eating disordered behaviours, and as such, BN, AN, EDNOS or other forms of restrictive eating disorders should not be differentiated in the way they are classified. However, the fact that there is a push to reclassify BN as an addiction is a positive step in the right direction.

The resistance to reclassify eating disorders as a form of addiction comes down to money, power and politics in a medical industry that runs like any other large industry of its type. There are too many ongoing dangerous and stereotypical myths stemming from traditional views about eating disorders and how they should be treated that people with influence in the industry still ascribe to. It is my hope, though, that with time, the emergence of more neuroscience evidence and perhaps the retirement of some of the currently powerful, old-fashioned *experts*, this way of thinking about eating disorders as a form of addiction will become mainstream (yes, I am an optimist!).

### Research Supporting the Theory of Restrictive Eating Disorders as an Addiction

To highlight the view of eating disorders as a form of addiction, I will summarise a study that was published in 2022 in a prominent journal, *Frontiers in Psychiatry*[5]. The authors of this study propose that anorexia nervosa (AN) is a form of addiction relating to changes in dopamine, supporting the dopamine model discussed earlier.

Beeler and Burghardt (2022) use current research evidence and hypothesis based on expert knowledge to propose that dopamine has a key role in both the onset of AN and its longer-term entrenchment in what can be considered a two-stage process.

## The Two-Stage Model of Eating Disorders as an Addiction

In Stage One of the model, Beeler and Burghardt propose that calorie restriction, especially when combined with exercise, triggers an escalating spiral of dopamine, which acts as a *psycho-stimulant* triggering further restriction and exercise. This leads to the behavioural neuroplasticity (changes to the brain circuitry) needed for the person to establish and continue to reinforce weight loss behaviours.

Putting this into simpler terms, restriction and exercise cause a high dopamine release in the susceptible person, which makes them feel great. This drives them to seek more dopamine by repeating the same behaviours, with increasing amounts of exercise and restriction. Their brain then wires in these patterns of energy deficit creating behaviours as pleasurable and worthy of regular repetition.

The authors also speculate that people who exercise a lot at this early stage of the eating disorder may be at a greater risk from this *dopamine storm*. Vigorous exercise could contribute to the development of the eating disorder by driving dopamine levels higher, resulting in the person developing full-blown AN even faster.

Unfortunately, at this early stage of the development of the eating disorder, it's hard or even impossible to differentiate between someone who is merely *dieting* and someone who will go on to develop an entrenched eating disorder.

In Stage Two of the model, the authors propose that as with other forms of addiction, the initial high release of dopamine that established the addictive habits can ultimately cause a drop in dopamine function. They believe that chronic self-starvation behaviours, with ongoing repetition, will over time lead to a reversal in the initial surge in dopamine these behaviours created, and dopamine levels are instead either reduced or their action becomes impaired. This change in dopamine signalling leads to the behavioural inflexibility and full entrenchment of the typical behaviours seen in someone with an eating disorder. The authors describe this as being when:

*Hypodopaminergic function decreases behavioural plasticity, driving inflexibility and compulsivity.*

This is when the established behaviours become *locked in* within the brain and very resistant to change.

This second stage of the model explains why people with eating disorders are seemingly unable to stop their energy deficit–creating behaviours, when a normal *dieter* would not be able to continue to pursue them. A normal *dieter* will find that their survival-based drive to eat quickly overrides the initial feel-good dopamine release resulting from early weight loss.

The authors also make the point that a change in the role of dopamine can be caused by chronic stress. Acute stress, i.e., short-lived stress, increases dopamine function in the brain, but chronic stress actually decreases it. Therefore, in a person with an eating disorder, the chronic stress caused by persistent calorie restriction and low body weight is very possibly another factor that contributes to the second stage of the dopamine model.

Overall, Beeler and Burghardt (2022) state that their proposed model is the same process that is seen in other addictions. The behaviours are learnt and reinforced initially and over time become inflexible and highly resistant to change, interfering with other activities and social relationships.

### Linking the Two-Stage Eating Disorder Model to the Previous Addiction Models

This model of AN as a form of addiction ties in well with the addiction models that have already been discussed in the book.

Within the two-stage model, the behaviours seen in an eating disorder are learnt initially, reinforced and ultimately *locked in* in a way that is resistant to change. This supports the *deep learning* model of addiction.

Another recent study of people with eating disorders adds even more credibility to the theory that eating disorders are a form of addictive habit and deep learning. This study demonstrated that people with eating disorders use a different brain region (the dorsal striatum, which is the region that stores and drives habitual behaviours) when selecting the food they are going to eat[6]. People without eating disorders select their food using a brain region that is not driven by habit. This would indicate that restriction and food choice in people with eating disorders is a deeply learnt behaviour, initially learnt through reward but then embedded as a habitually driven process. The study also found that for people with eating disorders, food choice was tied to triggers, and less conscious effort was used in comparison to people without eating disorders. The researchers who carried out this study concluded that the strong habitual nature of eating disorder behaviours explains how and why they can become so entrenched.

The changes in dopamine described in the two-stage model for AN, in which there is an initial surge and then a drop, is also very similar to the dopamine *seesaw* model for addiction.

When undertaking research for this book, I had contact with Dr Anna Lembke, who created the dopamine *seesaw* model. I asked her thoughts on this two-stage model of eating disorders in relation to dopamine and the idea that eating disorders are a form of addiction. This was her response:

*The pleasure-pain balance in relation to dopamine can illuminate anorexia nervosa. Restriction and weight loss (pressing on the pleasure side of the balance) and the positive reflections of others in response to weight loss lead to increased dopamine. Over time, however, the brain adapts and more extreme measures are required to get the same levels of dopamine. As the weight loss becomes extreme, the pleasure-pain balance loses its capacity to respond and gets stuck on the pain side of the balance, i.e., the dopamine is depleted and the individual is stuck in the dopamine-deficit state, a state that is both painful and also drives continued drug-seeking, in this case more starvation and exercise. This research paper (by Beeler and Burghardt) also supports this hypothesis.*

Email from Dr. Anna Lembke

In conclusion then, please be reassured that considering eating disorders as a form of addiction is not just a hypothesis that I have picked up and run with without supportive science. There is existing research evidence backing up this model for eating disorders, and there are several key addiction experts who support it.

• • • ● • ● • • •

# The Role of the Body's Opioids in the Addictive Nature of Eating Disorders

So far, only brief reference has been made to the role of the body's natural opioids in the development of an addiction and eating disorders. This is a topic that's worth considering in more detail.

Opioids are most thought of as substances that people take either in the form of a medication, such as morphine for pain or diazepam (Valium) as a relaxant, or in the form of drugs of abuse, such as heroin. However, as well as the synthetic form of opioids a person can take, our bodies also create their own natural opioids, which are called endorphins or enkephalins. These are released to help alleviate pain, but they also have the same effects as the drug forms, stimulating feelings of high pleasure and reducing feelings of stress. The way in which opioids create these effects is by increasing the release of dopamine into the striatum, which, as discussed earlier, has a rewarding and reinforcing effect, driving habit formation and potentially resulting in addiction[7].

Within the model of eating disorders as a form of addiction, there has long been the theory that both *self-starvation* (or restriction) and bingeing, as well as excessive exercising and vomiting, cause the body to release its own natural endogenous opioids.

Studies have found that natural opioids are higher in people with eating disorders than those without. Therefore, it's proposed that people with eating disorders become addicted to this significant opioid release arising from their pursuit of the energy deficit-creating behaviours. These natural opioids add to the surge in dopamine, further increasing the likelihood of the rewarding and reinforcing brain changes that result in the full development of the eating disorder[8 91011].

It's perhaps irrelevant whether your brain is addicted to the release of the natural opioids from engaging in the disordered behaviours or whether it's a high dopamine release arising from energy deficit. It's very likely to be a combination of these factors. At the end of the day, the neurobiological changes in relation to deep learning, brain circuitry and dopamine imbalance are still the same, as are the actions required to overcome the eating disorder.

• • • ● • ● • • •

# What Else Can Make Eating Disorder Behaviours Initially So Rewarding?

When any addiction first develops, it's because of a very high reward response from initial engagement in the *drug*.

For someone susceptible to developing an eating disorder, their first engagement in behaviours leading to energy deficit will create a high endogenous opioid release and simultaneous surge in dopamine into their brain. This results in a powerful drive to repeat those behaviours. But what else can reinforce a high reward response to the *drug* of energy deficit?

Any *drug* that becomes addictive will create an extreme reward reaction, which triggers the brain to seek more of the same, for any of the following three reasons:

- Simply engaging in the *drug* in and of itself is very pleasurable and results in a high natural opioid release.

- Engaging in the *drug* solves a problem that the person has, which in itself creates pleasurable feelings.

- The brain perceives that the behaviour or substance protects the person from harm.

When you understand a restrictive eating disorder as an overall addiction to energy deficit—which means some degree

67

of weight loss has triggered the addiction—you could be for-given for thinking that people who develop restrictive eating disorders do so because they wanted to lose weight. Then, when they achieved that goal, their brain released a surge of feel-good chemicals that led to the ongoing, addictive nature of the behav-iours. This will be the case for some people but not for everyone.

There are several possible reasons why someone susceptible to an eating disorder might experience an even greater reward response when they initially engage in the behaviours that drive them into a state of energy deficit. As with any addictions, these will fall under one or more of the three reasons given above. Therefore, the initial weight loss or state of energy deficit will have either solved a problem, been very pleasurable and emo-tionally regulating in itself or their brain perceived it to protect them from harm.

To clarify this, a few examples are provided below:

- The behaviours leading to energy deficit—such as eat-ing less, beginning to exercise or purging—are high-ly rewarding, creating a flood of natural opioids and dopamine, and this alone pushes the brain to seek more of the same.

- The initial engagement in dieting and other weight loss behaviours, resulting in some weight loss, creates a pow-erful sense of achievement. This is often further rein-forced by compliments from others.

- The pursuit of goals—such as sports achievements, a

certain body size or shape or to fit in with peers and diet culture expectations—is highly rewarding when achieved, creating a desire for more.

- Some eating disorders arise when someone has an initial problem not at all related to weight or shape. An example is someone who has a true phobia of vomiting. They learn that avoiding food intake prevents vomiting. With a vomiting phobia, the brain perceives vomiting to be a direct threat, and so it will highly reward behaviours (through dopamine release) that ensure they avoid the perceived danger.

- Someone who is highly anxious or self-critical or a person with a trauma history can find that as they enter a state of energy deficit through eating restrictively or other weight control behaviours, the addictive nature has a powerful self-soothing effect, enabling them to feel *normal*.

There are any number of things that can reinforce the initial surge in dopamine when someone first engages in behaviours that lead to energy deficit. In all cases, the person's brain will have noticed what caused the reward response and latched onto it. As they repeated the behaviours to continue to experience the feel-good effects from them, the restrictive eating disorder became entrenched with behaviours that were incredibly hard to stop, even after they had become detrimental to their life.

## My Experiences

Applying the above to my own experiences of when I developed an eating disorder, the rewards initially stemmed from the behaviours themselves being more rewarding than my brain had anticipated and, to some extent, the behaviours solving a problem for me.

At the age of twenty-seven years, I had no dieting history, no significant exercise history and I was for all intents and purposes a young woman who had never paid much notice to diet culture. I loved eating, I had no significant body image issues and I just believed myself to be bad at sports, so I had never really bothered trying much in the way of exercise.

This changed when I, together with my then fiancé, decided, as many people do, that for our own fitness and general health, we would join a gym. I slowly became fitter and realised that exercise was something I could do. I understand now that this created an additional surge of dopamine, motivating me to exercise more. At this point my eating was still the same, which was abundant and largely dense! As my body shape changed due to the exercise, I started to get a few compliments from people, which triggered a bit more dopamine release. This motivated me to reflect more on what I was eating so that I could maintain the slight body and weight changes I had seen. I started to tentatively pay more attention to what I was eating and realised that this was something I could also do quite well. At this point, I now realise, I was creating an increasing state of energy deficit in my body, leading to even more rewarding dopamine and endogenous opioid release.

As a result of the surges of dopamine and endogenous opioids created by compliments from others, initial feelings of accomplishment and of course the state of energy deficit I had entered, my brain was quickly embedding circuits that made pursuing exercise and restrictive eating habitual.

Over time, my brain adapted to the rewarding effects that these surges of dopamine created. This left me needing to pursue my *drug* of energy deficit with more intensity for the same feeling or, as time went on, just to feel some degree of *normal*. I had fully developed a powerful restrictive eating disorder.

· • • ◗• ◖ • • ·

# The Power of Rituals

In the blog posts I have written over the years about eating disorders, I have frequently referred to the *rigid and ritualistic behaviours* that form a significant part of a restrictive eating disorder.

When you have an eating disorder, there is not only an addictive drive to eat restrictively and engage in compensatory behaviours, but the way you approach these behaviours is very often fixed, rigid and surrounded by ritualistic acts. These rituals themselves then take on an addictive nature. Not being able to follow usual patterns when it comes to where or how you engage in the behaviours can create distress and anxiety.

Examples of this include having ritualistic times of day that you will eat or needing to be seated in the same spot to consume the same foods in the same amounts. You might have rituals in relation to movement patterns that you feel compelled to engage in before eating or before going to bed. Purging by vomiting can be ritualised in terms of when, where and how, or compulsive walks need to follow the exact same route each time, again in a pattern that is best described as ritualistic.

These rituals don't make sense if you are *just* addicted to the direct pursuit of energy deficit. If that were the case, then as long as you were eating restrictively, whether you did so sitting at the table or in an armchair should not make a difference.

The same with movement. If you were *only* addicted to walking, then as long as you got your fix in terms of how far or fast you walk, the route taken should not matter. Therefore, there is definitely something deeper occurring to create these powerful rituals around the eating disorder's addictive behaviours.

Interestingly, deeply ingrained rituals surrounding an addictive behaviour are also common to other kinds of addiction. Time of day in which the addiction is engaged in, the location or the *tools* used with it can all become as important to the person as the behaviour or substance itself. It's also recognised that rituals can be emotional. It might be that being upset about something gives someone a reason to engage in their *drug*. This leads them to seek something to become angry or upset about and becomes part of their ritualistic pattern.

An example of this in relation to restrictive eating disorders might be engaging in thoughts about being *fat* which trigger feelings of greed and disgust. This becomes an automatic ritualistic pattern that precedes restrictive eating habits.

Rituals that are followed as part of an addictive pattern of behaviour are largely unconscious, and if questioned, most people will not know why it is that they feel they must do something in a particular way or in a certain place. However, once someone has started to engage in a ritual as part of an eating or addictive disorder, it can be very hard for them to then stop themselves from going on to get their full *fix*.

So why does your brain push you to follow the habits that form part of your eating disorder in such ritualistic ways?

Over time, the pursuit of your *drug* of energy deficit has become your brain's primary goal and highest priority. As the eating disorder became deeply entrenched, your days primarily focused on what, where and how you would restrict or compensate, to the point that other things that you once found pleasure in lost their meaning. Therefore, your brain had come to identify these behaviours as highly important, even crucial to survival. It's little wonder that your brain notices and puts high importance onto everything that surrounds them.

When you first eat a restrictive meal at a certain place at the table, your brain notices, registers this and recognises that this seat is a spot that is safe to eat the foods you will eat. The time of day a behaviour is undertaken is also picked up by your brain and registered as highly important. Taking a route on that compulsive walk once becomes another thing that your brain latches onto as *This route matters, it's safe and it ensures I can get the dopamine I crave.*

You engage in a highly addictive behaviour and the how, what, where, when or emotional state you are in as you do so are noticed by your brain. It will then ensure future pursuit of the same rewards are successful by driving you to repeat them in the same way in future. In this way, rituals become just as deeply embedded habitual and subconscious parts of the eating disorder as the overarching behaviours themselves.

When you are attempting to overcome an eating disorder, it's crucial to identify what the rituals are that surround the behaviours you engage in. As stated above, once you start to engage in a ritual that would usually end in full engagement with the compulsive behaviour, it's very hard to then apply the brakes and stop yourself. This is because your brain has started to release dopamine in response to the ritual, and it has begun to follow the deep and automatic brain circuits that drive the full behaviour.

Recognising rituals, labelling them and establishing ways to stop them before they begin is critical. This might simply involve moving the furniture so that the usual seat at the table that you use for meals is no longer available, or deliberately making plans for the times of day that you would usually engage in compensatory behaviours. These changes can make a big difference to whether you successfully abstain from the eating disorder's habitual pursuit of energy deficit.

Rituals surrounding addictions and eating disorders are powerful. Be mindful of them and how much pull they have, finding ways to remove them wherever you can.

• • • • • • • • • •

# The Amygdala and Withdrawal

When someone is not engaging in their *drug* as part of an addictive or eating disorder, they can experience negative emotions, high anxiety and some unpleasant physical effects—commonly referred to as *withdrawal symptoms*.

### Common Withdrawal Symptoms

The withdrawal symptoms commonly experienced by people overcoming eating and other addictive disorders include:

- Anxiety, stress and intense feelings of fear or panic;

- Insomnia and sleep difficulties;

- Agitation;

- Depression and despair;

- Mood swings;

- Irritability, anger, frustration and annoyance;

- Feeling overwhelmed by small things;

- Lack of focus or ability to concentrate (a sense of brain fog);

- Headaches and pains or stiffness to joints, muscles, teeth or the jaw;

- Fatigue or feeling weak;

- Flu-like sensations, fevers, nausea;

- Urges to engage in other compulsive behaviours or habits;

- Flashbacks to the addiction or difficult times in your past; and

- Thoughts of self-harm or suicide.*

*If these occur, professional help is needed immediately.*

### What Causes Withdrawal Symptoms?

Withdrawal symptoms arise from two different systems in the brain of someone with an addictive disorder[12] .

The first of these relates back to the dopamine seesaw. This can be thought of as the brain's reward system seesawing to a state of dopamine deficit, which in itself creates feelings of low mood, agitation, lack of motivation and despair.

The second of the systems that makes abstaining from addictive behaviours so uncomfortable is the brain's stress system, found in the amygdala region of the brain. The amygdala is commonly understood to be the fight-or-flight centre, from which fear responses arise. It's one of the oldest parts of the brain from an evolutionary perspective.

When someone stops engaging in their addiction, a number of stress neurotransmitters (brain chemicals) are activated and released within the amygdala. As withdrawal from an addiction kicks in, the brain's levels of natural opioids and endorphins also decrease, as do levels of another anxiety-reducing brain chemical called GABA. Therefore, not pursuing the addictive *drug* creates a rise in brain chemicals that promotes a stress response and a lowering in chemicals that usually elevate mood and reduce anxiety.

For you, this means that the negative symptoms of withdrawal you might experience when you are not engaging in the eating disorder behaviours or as you attempt to stop them altogether come from two powerful brain systems, as well as changes in levels of other key neurotransmitters. Understanding this will help you to understand why attempting to give up eating disordered behaviours can result in intense negative emotional states.

The significantly unpleasant and painful symptoms of withdrawal are often a strong driving force pushing people to continue to engage in the compulsive eating disordered behaviours. The need to alleviate these intense and painful symptoms drives them back to their eating disordered habits, sometimes multiple times a day.

Unfortunately, returning to the addictive behaviours to alleviate the negative withdrawal symptoms only becomes a vicious circle. The symptoms of withdrawal increase over time and so make it even harder to maintain abstinence in future.

However, if you do manage to go through the withdrawal symptoms and abstain from addictive behaviours for long enough, then the brain's levels of neurotransmitters will naturally return to their baseline levels. When this happens, your brain will slowly begin to find pleasure in other (healthier) pursuits once again.

### How Long Does the Withdrawal Process Take?

The timeline for withdrawal symptoms is different for everyone, and not everyone will experience the same withdrawal symptoms or to the same intensity. It's impossible to say that in days 1-14 you will experience these symptoms, then in days 15-30 you will experience this, and in months 2 and 3 this will happen.

Some people, as they initially abstain from the eating disorder behaviours, have a period of feeling okay, even good and exhilarated. This is commonly followed in later weeks of continued abstinence with some of the more negative withdrawal symptoms discussed above. Others experience negative symptoms from day one of abstinence. It's impossible to know what will happen in your case. Only one thing is certain: if you keep going and stay with the process, these symptoms will pass, and slowly you will begin to feel *normal*, hopeful and positive in ways you will appreciate all the more because of the journey you have been on.

---

1. Lipton DM, Gonzales BJ, Citri A. Dorsal striatal circuits for habits, compulsions and addictions. Front Syst Neurosci. 2019 Jul 18;13:28. doi: 10.3389/fnsys.2019.00028. PMID: 31379523; PMCID: PMC6657020.

2. Lewis M. Brain change in addiction as learning, not disease. N Engl J Med. 2018 Oct 18;379(16):1551-1560. doi: 10.1056/NEJMra1602872. PMID: 30332573.

3. Göller S, Nickel K, Horster I, Endres D, Zeeck A, Domschke K, Lahmann C, Tebartz van Elst L, Maier S, Joos AAB. State or trait: the neurobiology of anorexia nervosa—contributions of a functional magnetic resonance imaging study. J Eat Disord. 2022 May 31;10(1):77. doi: 10.1186/s40337-022-005 98-7. PMID: 35641995; PMCID: PMC9158182.

4. Lembke, A. (2021). Dopamine Nation: finding balance in the age of indulgence. [New York, New York], Dutton, an imprint of Penguin Random House LLC.

5. Beeler JA, Burghardt NS. The rise and fall of dopamine: a two-stage model of the development and entrenchment of anorexia nervosa. Front Psychiatry. 2022 Jan 11;12:799548. doi: 10.3389/fpsyt.2021.799548. PMID: 35087433; PMCID: PMC8787068.

6. Steinglass, JE, Walsh, BT. Neurobiological model of the persistence of anorexia nervosa. J Eat Disord 4, 19 (2016). https://doi.org/10.1186/s40337-016-0106-2.

7. Gianoulakis C. Endogenous opioids and addiction to alcohol and other drugs of abuse. Curr Top Med Chem. 2009; 9(11): 999-1015. doi: 10.2174/156802609789630956. PMID: 19747123.

8. Davis C, Claridge G. The eating disorders as addiction: a psychobiological perspective. Addict Behav. 1998 Jul-Aug; 23(4): 463-75. doi: 10.1016/s0306-4603(98)00009-4. PMID: 9698975.

9. Kaye, WH, Berrettini, WH, Gwirtsman, HE, Gold, PW, George, DT, Jimerson, DC, et al. (1989). Contribution of CNS neuropeptide (NPY, CRH, and beta-endorphin) alterations to psychophysiological abnormalities in anorexia nervosa. Psychopharmacol. Bull. 25, 433-438.

10. Kaye, WH, Pickar, D, Naber, D, and Ebert, MH. (1982). Cerebrospinal fluid opioid activity in anorexia nervosa. Am. J. Psychiatry 139, 643-645. doi: 10.1176/ajp.139.5.643.

11. Adams, J & Kirkby, RJ. (2002). Excessive exercise as an addiction: a review. Addiction Research & Theory, 10(5), 415-438.

12. (1) Substance Abuse and Mental Health Services Administration (US); Office of the Surgeon General (US). Facing Addiction in America: The Surgeon General's Report on Alcohol, Drugs, and Health [Internet]. Washington (DC): US Department of Health and Human Services; 2016 Nov. CHAPTER 2, The Neurobiology Of Substance Use, Misuse, And Addiction. Available from: https://www.ncbi.nlm.nih.gov/books/NBK424849/.

# Chapter Four

# How to Reprogram Your Brain to Overcome a Restrictive Eating Disorder

N ow that you understand the addiction model to eating disorders and what's happening in the brain when someone develops any addiction, it's time to look at the important part, which is how to overcome it.

For your brain to overcome an eating disorder, it needs to be given the opportunity to reprogram.

Think of your brain as a computer that has been hacked, so it now has programming that is harmful and very much unwanted. To get your computer running smoothly again, it will need to have the harmful programming removed and new programming written in. This new programming needs to be on par to what was there before your computer was hacked or, ideally, because technology has moved on, an improvement.

The same is true for your brain. Your brain has been hacked by an eating disorder. However, you can make changes to your brain that will override the systems that are driving the eating disorder behaviours. To do this, your brain needs the opportunity to replace the harmful wiring and programming with systems and circuits that will allow you to function without an addiction to energy deficit ruining your life.

There are two key ways in which your brain needs to be reprogrammed in order to overcome an eating disorder:

1.      Unwire the eating disorder circuits and wire in new circuits driving *healthy* new habits.

2.      Adjust the levels of some key neurotransmitters and brain chemicals back to a stable baseline.

These reflect the deep learning and dopamine models to addiction and the reprogramming needed for each. Due to how important these processes are to understand, they will each be explored in more detail.

## Reprogram Your Brain: *Deep Learning* to Rewire

First, a quick recap:

When you develop an addictive or eating disorder, your brain builds strong circuitry in the striatum. This is the brain region responsible for driving habits that push you automatically and habitually to pursue your *drug*. In addition to this, there is a loss of communication between your striatum and PFC in relation to the addictive behaviours, which results in your being less able to apply reason, judgment or impulse control to them.

However, in the same way that you developed this deep learning with the eating disorder, it is possible for you to create new learning and habits towards healthier pursuits. When new behaviours are learnt, creating new circuitry, and this is coupled with abstinence from following the brain circuits driving the eating disorder, the old circuits become unused. Over time, the connections between the neurons in those old circuits are *pruned out* by your brain. In eating disorder circles, this process is commonly referred to as the brain *rewiring*.

Of course, this description of what needs to happen inside your brain in relation to *rewiring* sounds simple on paper. In reality it's far from simple. Strong habits are not unlearnt quickly or easily because your brain is so used to following those pathways automatically, without conscious awareness. We also know that you have much less ability to apply reason, judgment or inhibition to these powerfully addictive habits, and so stopping yourself from engaging in them in the moment is a challenge, to say the least!

The brain learns very rapidly when high emotion, especially anxiety or fear, or high rewards (from dopamine) are attached to a behaviour. This is why addictions that were initially very rewarding or arose from an anxiety response can develop so quickly. The new behaviours you are developing to replace the addictive circuits will not have the same level of reward or calming impact as your old habits. This means that although it is possible to build new learning and habits into your brain circuitry, it will take more deliberate pursuit and ongoing repetition of them.

Very importantly, though, if you only take one thing from this part of the book, understand that many addiction experts believe that as addictive disorders are a form of *deep brain learning,* there is absolutely no reason why your brain cannot develop essential new learning and *unlearn* those old addictive habits. If you continue the pursuit of learning the new behaviours you want and abstain from the old habits for long enough, your brain will stop following the old circuits driving the disorder. It's also thought that the longer the old circuits remain unused, the more they will break down. There is no reason to believe that once you have overcome the eating disorder and developed new *deep learning,* you will remain at lifelong risk of relapse or should be considered to have a *chronic brain disease.* For many people who have overcome addictive disorders, the decision is made to abstain long term because they don't want to take any risk of relapse. When you have fully overcome the eating disorder, you can choose whether you will abstain from all the behaviours that were once part of the eating disorder for the rest of your life. The related topic of relapse prevention is discussed later in the book.

### Reprogram Your Brain: The Dopamine Reset

In Chapter 3, the dopamine model of addictions was described with the analogy of the dopamine *seesaw*. In summary, your brain likes to maintain a certain dopamine level. When dopamine goes above or below this level, your brain will try to bring it back to balance (homeostasis). If dopamine drops below this baseline point, you will feel uncomfortable, anxious or low in mood, and so your brain will push you to change your circumstances and find ways to get more dopamine. If dopamine goes above baseline, when you pursue something pleasurable, your brain will also attempt to restore homeostasis. To do this, it will drop your dopamine levels down but this time to a point that is the same degree of change from baseline as the rise had been. This will make you feel uncomfortable and want to repeat the pleasurable behaviour again.

The more you pursue experiences that increase dopamine (pleasure side of the balance), the higher your dopamine levels will become above baseline. But, just like a seesaw, what goes up must eventually come down, and so these elevated levels are adding more weight to the pain side of the balance. At some point the balance will need to swing to the same degree below baseline as the rise. The ongoing pursuit of your highly rewarding *drug* of energy deficit results in so much weight added to the pain side of the seesaw that you are left with an ever-increasing dopamine deficit. Now, whenever you are not pursing your *drug*, you experience those very uncomfortable withdrawal symptoms. Furthermore, when you do engage in the behaviours, they no longer bring any meaningful sense of reward or pleasure, but engaging in them becomes the only way you have to feel normal.

For your brain to fully reprogram, not only does it need to rewire the circuitry, but a dopamine reset is also essential. The best way to establish this is to abstain from the dopamine-chasing behaviours, i.e., the eating disordered behaviours.

When you do abstain from the eating disorder and the behaviours that give rise to the release of dopamine—which is currently your only way to feel *normal* enough to function—your brain's dopamine seesaw will swing down into the dopamine deficit state that has been deepening all the time that you have had an eating disorder. This is going to create inevitable withdrawal symptoms that can feel terrible. BUT, as long as abstinence is maintained for long enough, your brain will work hard to restore your natural dopamine levels. Your brain's inner dopamine seesaw is no longer weighted down on the side of pain but is back to the baseline level that your brain needs. When your dopamine levels return to homeostasis, your withdrawal symptoms will dissipate. As your brain becomes fully balanced again, you will feel emotionally more *normal* without the need to use behaviours that are driven by the eating disorder to achieve this. At this point, you will also find that you are able to experience pleasure in the smaller things in life again; things that became disinteresting when you were walking around with chronically low dopamine levels.

When you go through a dopamine reset, it will also teach you more about the eating disorder and the addictive nature of your behaviours. As dopamine levels slowly return to a level balance, many people begin to understand that the eating disorder was not relieving their anxiety as they so often believed; it was actually the very thing causing that anxiety in the first place.

How long does it take for dopamine levels to reset and the brain to return to homeostasis?

The answer to this question will be different for everyone, and of course many individual factors will come into play. Dopamine levels can start to naturally return within weeks of abstinence, but don't forget that reprogramming the brain is a two-step process. Therefore, even if dopamine is restored within two or three months of abstinence, this is not a green light to return to old habits. The rewiring process takes a significant period of abstinence and time to build new circuits, so hang in there.

Once again, the good news here is that dopamine levels can be reset, and chemical imbalances driving the eating disorder can be reprogrammed. There is nothing chronically broken. Yes, it takes time—it takes going through inner pain and emotional turmoil for which time out and significant support might well be needed—but it can happen for you, just as it can for others.

To fully reprogram your brain and overcome the eating disorder, you need to change your habits. This means abstaining from the highly addictive eating disorder behaviours for long enough to allow deep learning of new behaviours to become programmed into your brain circuitry and to form new habits. As you abstain from the behaviours that were also creating a deep dopamine deficit in your brain, you will also be allowing it the time it needs to reset your dopamine levels so that you no longer carry so much anxiety and inner pain around with you.

All of this is possible. It takes hard work. It means going against strongly automatic old habits to which you have difficulty applying rational reasoning. It means experiencing emotional pain that you have pushed deep within yourself through the eating disorder for what is likely to be years, possibly decades. Therefore, this is going to be the hardest thing you are likely to ever do in your lifetime. Support and time out from other life demands will be needed, but if you are strong enough to have lived with an eating disorder for any amount of time, you are strong enough to overcome it too.

• • • ● • ● • • •

# Reprogram Your Brain - Abstinence or Moderation?

The eating disorder has made your life too miserable to live with any longer. Perhaps it has destroyed your relationships, impacted your social life, removed your ability to experience pleasure in small things, affected your work or studies, led you to behave in ways that go against your values, made you physically weak and depleted or living with perpetual anxiety and low mood. You know you are done with the eating disorder and want to find a future life that's free from those addictive and compulsive behaviours. You now understand that you need to *reprogram* your brain to achieve this—but how?

In the previous section, a brain-based explanation was provided as to why abstaining from engaging in your *drug*, rather than moderating use is often the best approach to overcome it. Abstinence gives your brain the chance to fully reprogram both in terms of rewiring circuits and to reset your dopamine levels, so those miserable withdrawal symptoms (the high anxiety, low mood, agitation and irritability) subside sooner rather than later. When dopamine can fully reset in your brain, it's restorative, and you will feel so much better.

But is abstinence the only approach?

When it comes to overcoming an eating disorder, can a moderated approach be used, rather than abstaining fully from those energy deficit-creating behaviours and associated rituals?

What does abstinence in relation to restrictive eating disorders even mean and how does it differ from a moderation approach?

In the next section I aim to answer these questions, exploring what an abstinence approach in overcoming an eating disorder looks like and how it differs from a moderation approach. Reasons why you might choose one approach over another are also explored.

•  •  •  ●  •  ●  •  •  •

# Reprogram Your Brain from a Restrictive Eating Disorder with an Abstinence Approach

The best approach to overcome an addiction and therefore an eating disorder is to abstain from all the behaviours related to it for a sustained period. The reasons for this in relation to what needs to happen within your brain have been given. There are also other reasons as to why abstinence can be preferable.

### It Is Mentally Easier to Abstain

People who have overcome an eating or other addictive disorder widely report that abstaining from their *drug* altogether is mentally easier to manage. When you decide to cut back instead of abstaining, you are still giving yourself permission to *use the eating disorder behaviours but less often*. This can take a lot more mental energy as you try to work out how much restriction you will eradicate and how much you will continue, as well as where the boundaries come in with other behaviours. It takes mental focus and stamina to keep saying *no more* to yourself within the limits you have set. While you are continuing to use the eating disordered brain circuits and pursue behaviours that elevate your dopamine levels, the urges and cravings for more will be more powerful.

When you abstain, it will give you a lot more clarity when you reflect on your behaviours and how big the problem really is.

This can be hard to recognise when you are still pursuing your *drug,* even if to a lesser degree.

Through abstinence, you can apply black–and–white rules to the eating disordered behaviours, which provides more clarity for both you and anyone supporting you. You just don't engage in them.

During the time I spent in eating disorder treatment, we were frequently told that those of us with eating disorders have *black–and–white thinking.* This used to irritate me, as it was another way treatment can fail to look at the individual and instead tarnish anyone with an eating disorder with the same brush. However, when it comes to abstaining from the eating disorder, whether you usually have black–and–white thinking or not, applying it to the abstinence approach can certainly help.

### Abstinence Removes Any Feel–Good *Hits*

The other reason that people generally find abstaining easier than *cutting back* is that when you are continuing to engage in the eating disorder behaviours, you are effectively continuing to take your *drug* and getting that *hit.* When you are still taking your drug, your brain will want more each time, which makes sliding back to a full relapse a much higher risk. In this way, you are dealing with strong, ongoing urges that you are going to have to work hard to resist each day.

When you fully abstain, it stops your brain from getting these *hits* that activate stronger cravings, allowing your brain time to stop creating those powerful urges and reprogram more effectively.

### The Idea of Abstinence Can Be Overwhelming

The thought of abstaining fully from the eating disorder will feel overwhelming. You might be able to understand all the reasons why it's the best approach, but you just can't envision how you will cope, what will happen or where it will take you.

At this point, avoid jumping ahead. Decide to abstain today and take it one day at a time or even half a day at a time if that helps. The person you will be tomorrow or a week from now is not the same as the person you are today. Just focus on what you can manage today and what you need to do to abstain from the eating disorder in every way possible in the here and now.

Your brain needs a rest from the constant bombardment of following all the eating disordered habitual thoughts and behaviours so that it can reprogram. Decide that you will treat your brain to the best reprogramming software available and do it.

One final word before getting into the nitty-gritty on how to abstain from the eating disordered behaviours. This is to those of you thinking that this doesn't apply to you because, *I have never restricted that much. I don't do much exercise. I only purge a couple of times a week. My weight is actually not that low;*

*it is even considered a "healthy" weight.* If you have any level of restrictive eating disorder that's having a negative impact on your life and you haven't been able to stop the related behaviours because of how compulsive they are, then this applies to you just as much as it does to anyone else. Do not listen to thoughts telling you otherwise.

• • • ● • ● ● • •

# How to Abstain from a Restrictive Eating Disorder

If you have read this far and you are still with me, then great. Grab a cuppa and a few donuts and let's continue.

I imagine you are now keen to know how to abstain from the eating disorder. After all, it is a little more complicated than abstaining from other addictions such as drugs, gambling or Internet gaming. Abstaining from restrictive eating probably sounds like a confusing concept, while giving up all compulsive movement impossible.

It's true that abstaining from a restrictive eating disorder takes a little more creative thinking, but it's not that complicated. It takes logical thought and going against everything you feel is right, not to mention many of the things that today's diet culture attempts to brainwash us with. However, there are definite ways through, and you can find them.

If a restrictive eating disorder is an addiction to the state of energy deficit, then what's the opposite?

The opposite is energy surplus and the deliberate pursuit of it, which means disengaging from any behaviours that create, maintain or increase an energy deficit state. These are typically behaviours that could make you lose weight or that control your weight at a level below your set weight range. You then need to engage in behaviours that will have the opposite effect, which is a state of energy surplus. And yes, this does mean necessary weight gain so that your body can restore energy balance.

When you understand abstinence from a restrictive eating disorder in this way, you can begin to apply it in practical terms. This, of course, does take courage. It will go against every fibre of your body and a lot of the diet-influenced teachings you have encountered to not just stop behaving like you are on a mission to lose weight but to behave as if you are deliberately pursuing weight gain. However, no one said that this process would be easy or feel right.

At the moment you are probably still feeling overwhelmed and unsure about what is expected when it comes to abstaining from the eating disorder. Therefore, let's break it down into some of the most common behaviours seen in people with restrictive eating disorders.

There are some common restrictive eating disorder behaviours for which abstinence rules are easy to apply:

- Purging through vomiting

- Weighing yourself

- Chewing and spitting

- Weighing and measuring foods

- Calorie counting

- Using a Fitbit or other device to track anything

Any behaviours that can be stopped and that you can apply simple black-and-white abstinence rules to, you do so. I am not saying stopping these things will be easy, but have these clear rules for yourself.

• • • • • • • • • •

## Abstaining from Restriction

For many people, restrictive eating has become so habitual that they fail to grasp the concept of what *normal* or unrestricted eating looks like. To then be able to picture unrestricted eating in someone coming out of an energy deprived state is even harder. I have now worked with enough people who believe that eating a tiny bit more for breakfast and one extra small snack a day is an extreme form of unrestricted eating. This might sound laughable, but it's entirely understandable when you consider where they are coming from. Compared to their years of rigid, restrictive eating, never eating a single raisin above their habitual amounts, eating anything more, however small, feels extreme. To override this potential mental block so that you do fully abstain from restrictive eating and not just toy with an extra small snack a day, it will be valuable to take some time to reflect and prepare.

Perhaps the most effective way of abstaining from all restriction is to take a step back and remove yourself from the scenario. While you are at the centre of things, your emotional response and your brain trying to hold on to the addictive behaviours will get in the way. Instead, imagine you are advising someone who needs to do the absolute opposite to eating as if they are on a diet. What would you advise them to do? What would Joe Bloggs on the street advise if this question were put to him?

The answers that come will be exactly what's needed to abstain from restriction.

If someone needs to do the absolute opposite to eating as if they are on a diet, they need to be eating most of the time and predominantly high-fat, high-calorie, dense foods. They should be having big meals and lots of snacks. There would be no avoidance of processed foods or fast foods. All food groups and food types would be recommended but with an understanding that high density is better, and nothing should be avoided other than diet products. They would not count calories or have limits, and they would be eating like a person who didn't care a fig about weight gain!

If you keep asking yourself what a person who is doing the opposite to someone on a diet would do, someone wanting to GAIN weight, then the answers will lead you to the action you need to take to abstain from restriction.

This mindset also overcomes the difficulties people have in trying to understand how much they *should* be eating or what the *right* amounts to eat are. If you aim to eat like a person pursuing weight gain and not attempting to control the rate of gain, then you can begin to understand what abstaining from all restriction really means. The only *right* amounts to eat are as much as you could be eating.

The other benefit to this approach is that it also addresses a lot of the smaller behaviours and rituals, such as only eating at certain times of day. After all, if you were deliberately aiming for weight gain, removing any limits on your eating, why would you wait to eat?

It's also a faster way to overcome your other rules around eating, for example rules about how much you are *allowed* at each meal or limits you have set on fat or carbs. All these rules and restrictions are pushed out through the abstinence approach because a person doing the opposite to someone on a diet would not have rules like these. Get into the *aim to gain* mindset, and it will lead you to the exact things you need to do to abstain from all restriction and restrictive behaviours.

Now you might be thinking, *But I don't want to gain weight,* or *I am scared to gain weight.* In my experience, most people deal a lot better with any weight gain than they think they will. But at the end of the day, this process is about overcoming a powerful eating disorder to make your life worth living. Weight gain is a necessary part of that process as it takes your body out of the energy deficit state you are in and that your brain is addicted to. Therefore, this approach is a good way to ensure you are abstaining from all the restrictive behaviours and habits that maintain the eating disorder's addictive grip.

This is also the method that will enable your brain to fully unwire all the old circuits that drive the restrictive behaviours—because you will no longer be pursuing them—whilst wiring in circuits that will help you create new habits related to unrestricted eating. Any weight gain that happens as a result is a side effect to claiming your health and freeing your life. Chapter 10 covers a lot more information about weight gain, including set weight theory and fat overshoot.

### A Few More Tips to Abstain from Restrictive Eating

As you pursue the abstinence approach to your usual restrictive eating, you might need to establish a few more ground rules if you are struggling to get into the *abstinence* mindset straight away. If this is the case, here are a few suggestions for some additional black-and-white rules to follow in your pursuit of abstinence from all restriction:

- Set yourself a high baseline amount of food that you will eat every day no matter what. This is the minimum that you eat, even if your head is convincing you that you aren't hungry or that you don't *need* it or if you have people dieting around you making you feel *greedy*. Your baseline food intake needs to be HIGH. To allow deep learning to occur in terms of eating without any restriction, it can be helpful to go to the other extreme for a while. For many people, aiming high really is easier to understand than trying to eat to appetite or in more moderate amounts, especially at the beginning of the process. It's also beneficial because when your body is malnourished, it needs the food, and eating high amounts tells your brain that any famine situation it perceived is now over. It will then start to create the deep hunger signals that it always wanted to send. Once these hunger signals come, allow them to drive you onwards.

- When setting your high baseline amount of food, a meal plan isn't necessary. Meal plans in themselves are frequently too restrictive and provide too much structure; they then become fixed, rigid and hard to break. To set a high baseline amount, choose a method that works for you. Calorie counting is not advisable, as that's another eating disorder behaviour. If you don't already count calories, starting to do so in trying to overcome the eating disorder is also not a good idea. Exchange methods are also too rigid and unnecessarily complicated (eating shouldn't be complicated). Instead, have a mental image of what your intake should be. You might work with a coach or a good dietician (someone who supports full, unrestricted eating) to establish this. This baseline amount of food doesn't need to be written out in a planned way or overly structured and is the minimum general amount that you eat every day, always ensuring it is your absolute minimum. Remember, the idea here is to abstain from all restriction. More is only going to help your brain reprogram more effectively and efficiently, so never hold back.

- From your baseline amount of food, eat to any hunger above it. If you recognise any signs of hunger, whether they are physical, mental, emotional or behavioural, then you should be eating. Not eating when your body is sending you hunger signals is restriction. You are abstaining from restriction, so you eat to all hunger. In the accompanying handbook, there is guidance on all the ways hunger can manifest beyond the physical symptoms commonly thought of. Please refer to this if you need to.

- If in doubt, eat. If you are not sure if you have hunger or not, then you probably do—people who aren't hungry don't usually have to question it. Either way, you are abstaining from restriction to overcome the addiction your brain has to energy deficit, so it's always safer to eat when you are questioning your hunger level than not eat.

- When extreme hunger hits, let it take you as high as it needs to. Chapter 10 provides more information on extreme hunger and what causes it.

- Recognise the habitual ways in which you use restrictive behaviours in your day-to-day life, beyond the obvious.

In the accompanying handbook there is information about all the ways that restriction can manifest, so if you need to, please refer to this and identify what is true for you. Write out all your usual restrictive habits and then create black-and-white rules for each to help you address them. An example of this might be that you have started to eat toast with peanut butter, but you will only allow yourself one spoonful of peanut butter on each slice of toast, even though you would like more. That's a restrictive rule and habit that needs to go. Make a new black-and-white rule for this. For example, when making toast and peanut butter, I will slather the peanut butter on abundantly, making it at least an inch thick.

- Develop skills in being honest with yourself and with those supporting you. Whenever you finish eating something, ask yourself, *Could I eat more right now?* If you could still be putting food in your mouth and physically eating, then the answer is yes. Therefore, eat more. You will have to be very honest with yourself on this. Your brain is automatically wired to eat restrictively and go down the automatic thought pathways of, *I am done; I'm not hungry; it's not time to eat* or *No one else is eating more.* You need to ignore all these thoughts and be black and white. *I could be eating more right now, so I will.* Keep it simple. As I say, be honest with those supporting you too, so they can reassure you and help you through the process, encouraging you to keep eating despite the automatic restrictive thoughts and urges.

Abstain fully from restriction by taking on the *aiming to gain* mindset.

At the beginning of the process, most people are unable to connect to their hunger signals, whether they are mental, physical or in any other form. After months or years of ignoring hunger signals, it isn't easy to recognise and interpret them correctly. Therefore, telling someone to abstain from restriction by eating to all their hunger is something they cannot always make sense of. What are those signs of hunger when they are showing up? How do you respond to them? What is an appropriate thing to eat when the hunger is there? All these questions can be confusing and overwhelming to navigate.

The abstinence approach—in which you act like a person fully intending to gain weight through behaviours that are the opposite to those a person on a diet or pursuing energy deficit would engage in—can be easier to comprehend and more effective. With time, this approach will help you to begin to understand your body's signals. The natural intuition of what hunger feels like, mentally and physically, is more comprehensible when you have experienced what true satiety and fullness feel like. When you reach this point, it's possible to continue the process of fully abstaining from any restriction by beginning to experiment with eating to hunger and appetite, using the signals your brain and body are sending. This means still eating all the good foods in completely non-restrictive ways but now with an increased ability to respond to mental and physical hunger signals, so that you relearn these skills too.

• • • ● • ● • • • •

# Abstaining from Compulsive Movement & Exercise

Many people with restrictive eating disorders develop some form of compulsive movement or exercise addiction. The way in which this manifests looks different for everyone and can change over time. Some people might go out running every day without fail, swimming or cycling, while others might walk the dog each day for twenty minutes or do low-level yoga twice a week. The amount of exercise you do is largely irrelevant. If the exercise or movement you engage in is compulsive and addictive—meaning it's hard to stop because doing so creates high anxiety or agitation—then it doesn't matter how intense it is or isn't. It's all just as valid. It's damaging your life and abstaining from it is the best way to overcome this addiction.

As with abstaining from any strong habits though, you will have more chance of success if you also ensure you are replacing the old movement or exercise-based habits with new habits you want to build. Therefore, decide on what you will do instead of going for a walk or cleaning the house that's sedentary and that will both distract you and become a new and happy habit. Eating can always be part of your alternative activity!

When it comes to abstaining from formal exercise, it's relatively easy to understand what to do and create black-and-white rules:

- Do no formal exercise at all.

- Do no walking that isn't essential. If you have a dog, arrange for someone else to walk it.

- Do no yoga, not even *gentle* forms.

- Do no cycling, even if you try to convince yourself that you must cycle to get from A to B. Use public transport, the car, Uber, or if you really can't, then stay home and rest.

Compulsive lower-level movement is another eating disorder behaviour that affects a large proportion of people. This involves compulsively engaging in things like doing the housework, keeping busy, moving around for the sake of it, fidgeting and standing when you could be sitting.

People with compulsive lower-level movement find it very hard to be still, sit down or generally relax their minds or bodies. These behaviours are addictive and unless addressed will prevent full unwiring and rewiring of the eating disordered brain circuitry and a full dopamine reset. However, it can be harder to establish how to abstain from these behaviours, especially when they are often insidious. Create rules for yourself in terms of the following:

- Only stand when necessary. If you find yourself standing up, ask yourself, *Could I be sitting now?* and if the honest answer is yes, then sit down.

- Ask other people to do the housework and general household or garden chores while you are in the process of overcoming the eating disorder. If you ask family to take on these chores and this makes you feel guilty, remind yourself that this is to allow you to overcome this powerful addictive eating disorder so that you can have better relationships with them and be more present for and with them in future. If you don't have family to help with chores, then consider hiring a cleaner or gardener while you are going through this process.

- If you really don't have anyone to help with chores and you honestly can't afford to pay for help, then set yourself clear limits for how long you will spend on chores a week and keep to it. It might be you allow yourself one hour of housework a week and no more than that. Your house does not need to sparkle. Overcoming the eating disorder is more important.

- When you prepare food, make a lot in one go and take it all with you to sit back down. This prevents you from constantly getting up and down to the kitchen with the excuse *I'm getting food, so it's okay.*

- If you have stairs in your home, bring everything downstairs at the start of the day that you will need for the remainder of it. If items need to go upstairs during the day, make a pile at the bottom of the stairs and take it all up together in the evening. Avoid going up and downstairs as an excuse to move.

- Reflect on your typical day hour by hour to identify where compulsive lower-level movement manifests for you. Make a list and then create solutions for each so that you can address them.

- If you go out, use the car and park as close as you can to where you are going. In the supermarkets, visit the aisles you need to buy things from and not all the others too. Observe ways you habitually move about more than you need to when you are out of the house and address them.

- Ensure family or support people in your life are aware of your lower-level movement compulsion. Many people who have never had eating disorders do not understand this pattern of behaviours or how addictive they are until they are told. They probably think you love housework and maybe talk about you fondly as someone who *can't sit down*. Help them understand that these compulsions are part of the eating disorder and discuss how they can support you in addressing and abstaining from them.

Exercise and lower-level movement can be incredibly addictive and compulsive, affecting most people with restrictive eating disorders to some extent. In my case, it was one of the hardest parts to give up, and it was the one aspect of the eating disorder that I never believed I would overcome. Happily, it is possible to overcome it, but it will not be easy.

Create clear rules for how you will abstain and find support for both accountability and to help you cope emotionally.

· · · **·** · **·** · · ·

## Laxatives, Diet Pills, Alcohol or Other Substances

It's not uncommon for people with restrictive eating disorders to habitually use laxatives, diet pills, alcohol or other substances. Abstaining from these with a *cold turkey* approach is not always medically advisable. Your body could have developed a physiological dependence on substances, and you may face significant physical effects that might even be dangerous if you stop them abruptly.

If you do have an addiction to any substances such as these, please speak to a medical practitioner about the best way to address this. You might need a program to reduce them gradually or some other forms of medication to reduce any risks associated with stopping them.

●

# Addressing the Question of Binges

I know that some of you reading this will be asking, What about binges? Do I need to abstain from the binges*?

When you have a restrictive eating disorder and experience episodes of binge eating, the binges are being caused by the fact that your body is in a state of energy deficit. Restrictive eating and compensatory behaviours that keep your body in energy deficit ultimately give rise to these episodes of binge eating. Binges are an animal response, triggered by your brain to ensure survival. It's your brain taking over and deciding that no matter what else, food is needed now and as a matter of urgency. People who have experienced binges will usually describe their inability to control them, and many talk about *zoning out*. A common analogy used to understand binge eating is that it's like when you have held your breath for too long. Sooner or later your brain and body take over, and you can't stop yourself from drawing in a huge intake of air. This is what a binge can feel like, only with food.

It's true that binges can have addictive qualities and possibly some similar neurobiological processes behind them. Binges can often also be ritualistic and even enjoyed or looked forward to. However, the way to address them is not by abstinence.

In all likelihood, because of how strong the drive to binge is and the power behind it, you would have great difficulty stopping yourself if you tried, but happily you don't need to. If you address the restriction and the other behaviours that are creating the energy deficit, getting your body out of its energy deficit state, then the drive to binge will naturally recede.

The take-home message when it comes to binge eating is don't attempt to abstain from the binges. Leave them be and address all the other addictive behaviours that cause them.

*Please note that this is about true binges, not extreme hunger eating. Eating to extreme hunger is something people can control and isn't the same as binge eating. See Chapter 10 for more on this.*

• • • • •• • • • • •

# Avoiding the Lure of Your Rituals

The role and power of rituals in relation to eating disorders were discussed in Chapter 3.

As soon as you start to engage in a ritual that triggers a full behaviour, your brain has started to follow the old familiar eating disordered circuits. Dopamine driving the full pursuit of the *drug* is pumping out, creating strong cravings to keep going. This means that it's now much harder to put the brakes on, stop the behaviour in its tracks and divert your course of action.

For this reason, when you are planning how you will abstain from the eating disordered behaviours, it's crucial that you also consider the rituals that trigger each of them. These might be time-of-day rituals, crockery and cutlery that you have to use or certain actions you feel compelled to carry out before you will prepare food or purge. Perhaps you have body-checking rituals that drive *fat* thoughts and related emotions, which then trigger you to engage in movement compulsions.

Identify all the rituals you can that surround the eating disorder and list them. Then you can put measures in place to stop yourself from automatically heading down one of these ritualistic paths. This will ultimately make it easier to abstain from the deeper addictive behaviours.

Rituals are strong habits, and habits are automatic and can be hard to break. However, breaking them is going to be essential for you to overcome the eating disorder, so it's crucial to address them. When overcoming an eating disorder, change everything about your day, your routines and your habits. In doing so you are more likely to address not just the full behaviours but also these rituals that can trigger them.

• • • ● • ● • • •

# What to Expect in the Abstinence Process

Some indication of what to expect when you go through the abstinence process to overcome a restrictive eating disorder has already been provided in other sections. Let's explore this in a bit more detail.

It is first important to remember that everyone is different in terms of their experiences and the symptoms they encounter when overcoming an eating disorder. This section provides general information in terms of what CAN happen. That's not to say that all the symptoms described here WILL happen. It's also possible that you will experience symptoms that aren't covered here.

Starting the abstinence process is going to be very difficult for most people, although not all. For some, the realisation of just how awful their life has become with the eating disorder is enough motivation to push them with a *gung-ho* and hopeful attitude into the process of abstinence, and they find the first week or two a relief, even exhilarating.

For others, perhaps those who have attempted *recovery* numerous times before and never made meaningful progress, there might be a more weary and less optimistic start to the process. This is understandable and people in this situation are likely to find it harder from the beginning.

At the beginning of the reprogramming process, your brain is going to try hard to continue to find the intense *fix* of dopamine it associates with the eating disordered behaviours you habitually engage in. Your brain also has very strong circuitry that links any distress you feel with the short-term relief of following those addictive behaviours. Your brain has also developed powerful links between certain triggers that you encounter in your daily life—such as seeing a set of scales, a time of day you usually eat or go for a walk or a certain person or place—with the *fix* it gets from restriction, purging or other behaviours. The only way to weaken all these links in your brain circuitry is to stop using and reinforcing those circuits. However, this also means not getting the *fix* of dopamine that makes you feel normal enough to function.

If you abstain for long enough, learning new behaviours as you do so, the connections in the circuits driving the addictive behaviours will weaken, while new circuits build and become stronger (unwiring and rewiring).

Unfortunately, in the short term, disengaging from the eating disordered behaviours is going to leave you feeling anxious, depressed, agitated, distressed and possibly hopeless at times. You may experience emotional pain like you have never had before, which will give you powerful urges to run straight back to get an instant fix from the eating disorder. Triggers in your day-to-day life will try to pull you into old habits. To prevent yourself from being lured back when the urges become overpowering you will need a lot of support and to put definite measures in place.

Over time, as you continue to abstain from the old behaviours and develop new habits, your brain will have a chance to unwire the old circuits and wire in new ones. It will also establish a dopamine balance that gives you a level sensitivity to experiences of pleasure and pain.

When you were deep in the eating disorder, your brain was no longer capable of feeling pleasure in very much at all. Even usual levels of sadness or negative emotions would have been lost to you as you numbed them out with the compulsive behaviours. The further you move through the abstinence process, the more you will find that small things in life are pleasurable and even fun. You should begin to naturally smile more and find yourself less serious, hopefully laughing a bit more every day.

As you keep going and your brain continues to fully reprogram, it gradually gets easier. Urges to go back to the old behaviours will become less intense and less frequent the more you resist them and find new ways of coping. You will develop and perfect skills at recognising the urges when they arise more rapidly and blocking them with greater ease.

People often say that over time the old habits fade but still linger, manifesting now and again as a fleeting thought about them or even a, *shall I?* However, if this thought does occur, it is with significantly less craving to engage in the old behaviour and no longer with the belief that this path is your only choice.

## Progress Is Not Linear, & Lapses Are Normal

By now you have learned that the reprogramming process to overcome an eating disorder can create some intense and difficult emotional and physical symptoms.

These symptoms are not going to subside after a day or even a week. This is a process that takes time. Cravings, tears, anxiety, fear and panic can all be intense at times, but remember, this is normal and part of the process.

On the positive side, most people experience good and bad days with the withdrawal symptoms and cravings. Many people also experience moments of exhilaration when they have a real *win* over the eating disorder and do something that it had stopped them from doing for years. Some people also find that really good days and not great days can follow one another, which is when it feels that your emotions are on a roller coaster. This is a sign that the brain chemicals that affect your mood and emotional stability are attempting to normalise but swinging too far in one direction or the other as they try to find the middle ground.

Whilst going through all these emotions, withdrawal symptoms and cravings, it's possible there will be times when you find it impossible to resist the urge to use the behaviours again in one form or another. In all likelihood, you will also have times when the habitual nature of the behaviours has pulled you in before you even realised what's happened. Lapses are inevitable in this process. Don't aim for them but at the same time, don't beat yourself up when they do happen. There is certainly no shame to them. Every lapse is a learning opportunity to ensure that the same situation can be avoided in future. Overall, stay persistent in your approach but forget about perfection!

There is more information on lapses and relapses in Chapter 13.

• • • ● • ● • • •

# Complications of *Refeeding*

Before you rush off to dive into your abstinence approach to beat the restrictive eating disorder out of your life...a few words about refeeding.

## Refeeding Syndrome

When you are contemplating starting the process to overcome a restrictive eating disorder and abstaining from the restricted level of eating that your body is used to, it's important to know about the possible complications that can arise as you *refeed*. For some people, there is a risk of something called *refeeding syndrome* in the first few days or weeks of beginning to eat more. Although not very common, when it does occur, refeeding syndrome can be serious and, in some cases, can result in death. This section is not to frighten you though or give you a reason to continue to restrict in the way you have been. This information is to make you aware of any risks that could be relevant as you start the process of eating more so that you can take the necessary steps to proceed safely.

Refeeding syndrome was first described after World War Two in people released from concentration camps where they had faced prolonged periods of semi-starvation. In most cases, refeeding syndrome starts in the first four to seven days when a person who has been malnourished begins to eat more.

There is no clear and recommended definition for refeeding syndrome, but it's commonly understood to be a combination of hormonal and metabolic changes in people who have been nutritionally debilitated and who are *fed too fast*. Water and electrolyte imbalances are observed, particularly noticed as significant drops in certain electrolytes. A drop in blood phosphate levels is the most widely recognised diagnostic marker, but drops in potassium, sodium, magnesium, calcium and thiamine can also occur. There are also shifts in blood glucose levels.

### What Causes Refeeding Syndrome?

When your body is in a state of ongoing hunger, insulin levels drop and glucagon levels rise. The body adapts to this insufficient energy intake by using alternative energy sources for essential functions—switching from the use of glucose as the main energy source to using fatty acids and amino acids for energy instead. These are obtained from the breakdown of fat and muscle. If after a period of starvation your body is then given a large amount of food, insulin levels increase, leading to a rapid shift of potassium, magnesium and phosphorus into the cells. However, because of the body's malnourished state, it has insufficient supplies of these electrolytes to cope with this shift and so it leaves low levels of them in the circulating bloodstream. These electrolyte deficiencies in the blood result in the complications that can occur in refeeding syndrome. You can also experience a rise of blood glucose levels and a drop in thiamine (vitamin B$_1$).

## What Are the Signs and Symptoms of Refeeding Syndrome?

Refeeding syndrome can present with a range of symptoms. Some people experience mild symptoms, but for others these can become very serious.

Below are some of the key symptoms to observe for:

- Muscle weakness

- Abnormal heart rhythms

- Oedema (water retention)

- Chest pain

- Nausea and vomiting

- A drop in blood pressure or heart rate

- Feeling very light-headed

- Confusion

- Muscle spasms

- Muscle cramps

- Fatigue

- Shortness of breath

- Balance or coordination difficulties

- Heart failure

- High blood sugars, which can also cause:

-     headaches
-     blurred vision
-     frequent urination

The most common cause of death from refeeding syndrome results from abnormal heart rhythms.


**Who Is Most at Risk?**

Refeeding syndrome doesn't just affect people who are overcoming restrictive eating disorders. The risk is present in anyone who has been malnourished and then begins to *refeed*. Some of the additional risk factors are:

- Recent weight loss of more than 10 percent of body weight;

- Severely restricted food intake in the past 7–14 days;

- A person with a restrictive eating disorder or someone with signs of starvation syndrome;

- Frequent self-induced vomiting;

- Chronic alcohol use; and

- Chronic overuse of laxatives or diuretics.

A key point to also note is that refeeding syndrome can happen to anyone at any BMI. It is not just people with a low BMI who are at risk. People with a BMI in the *overweight* or *obese* categories can also develop refeeding syndrome, with risks of the same consequences.

Anyone who is beginning to eat more after a period of restrictive eating should be aware of refeeding syndrome and the symptoms to look out for. However, those who currently have a very low daily intake, have sustained significant weight loss in the past six months, who purge through vomiting regularly or who abuse laxatives or diuretics should be more cautious in the first week or two of increasing their intake. Refeeding syndrome is less likely in a person whose weight has been stable in recent months (even if stable at a point significantly below their set point) and in people who still eat regularly, even though that intake is restrictive.

Those who consider themselves to be above a low risk of refeeding syndrome (speak to a professional about your potential risk if you are unsure) should arrange for monitoring. This will involve regular blood tests to check levels of phosphate, potassium, magnesium and kidney function in the first few weeks of increasing energy intake.

## What Can Be Done to Prevent Refeeding Syndrome?

One of the key ways to help prevent refeeding syndrome is to be aware of your risk. If you think you are at risk or are unsure, speak to a health professional or eating disorder expert. Some people might be prescribed supplements, including thiamine and multi-vitamins, to take during the initial refeeding process. Your primary care team can also ensure you are having regular blood tests as you begin to eat more in order to monitor your electrolyte levels and pick up on any changes quickly so they can be treated. It's not always possible to prevent refeeding syndrome from occurring, but recognising the signs and symptoms early and being monitored will help ensure that if it happens, it's treated in time.

Traditionally, the advice has been to *start low and go slow* when reintroducing nutrition to someone who is at risk of refeeding syndrome, but some experts now doubt this approach. The risk of this slow approach to refeeding is that it can then result in *underfeeding syndrome,* where the individual loses weight because the approach is too cautious, resulting in further risk of complications from malnutrition. There is also now research demonstrating that more rapid refeeding can be safe, assuming phosphate levels are monitored[1]. However, the initial diet in the first week should ideally include less refined sugars (although these are great for the process beyond this!) and adequate levels of proteins and fats.

# Fluid Retention and *Weight* Gain

The complications of refeeding for most people will be uncomfortable (physically and mentally) but will not put them at medical risk.

Fluid retention affects a lot of people as they start the process of abstaining from restriction. This swelling and bloating can reinforce the thoughts that eating just a fraction more makes you gain weight overnight. The fluid retention is caused by changes in your blood sodium levels and glycogen stores because of eating more. It is also due to your body becoming rehydrated as many who are malnourished are also dehydrated. As you start to eat more, this gain in what is commonly referred to as *water weight* can cause a bigger jump in the numbers on your scales, seemingly overnight. If this does happen and you are weighing yourself or being weighed, remember that this rise is due to fluid shifts and not true weight change. The swelling and bloating—commonly seen in the ankles, around the eyes and face and around the midsection (although other areas of the body can also be affected)—will gradually improve, but this can take several weeks.

# Abdominal Discomfort

When your body has been restricted of essential energy and nutrients, it puts a low priority on maintaining and repairing the intestinal system as it preserves its precious energy supplies to keep more vital organs functioning. Therefore, your stomach and intestines are going to need some vital repairs before they can work optimally for you. But this is a chicken-and-egg situation; to get the energy into your body so that it can do those repairs, there needs to be extra food intake into a stomach that is not yet able to digest at its best. This means that as you begin to eat more, your stomach is going to have slow emptying, which can lead to feelings of nausea, stomach cramps, bloating, wind and constipation, as well as feelings of physical fullness on what are still small amounts of food. You will need to push past this and keep eating to get the much-needed energy and to begin the process of abstinence from restriction. At this stage you are likely to experience a confusing mix of new hunger but also excessive fullness. It's also important to be aware that anxiety and stress related to the process of overcoming the eating disorder are potential appetite suppressants and can exacerbate abdominal symptoms such as nausea and cramps.

Eating regularly and avoiding whole and unprocessed foods can help with the digestion, especially at the beginning of the process. Stay with it, keep eating and things will all start working well in no time.

# Reprogram Your Brain from a Restrictive Eating Disorder with a Moderation Approach

So far, this chapter has explained the reasons why abstaining from all eating disordered behaviours to allow your brain to fully reprogram is considered the best approach. When you fully stop the behaviours, you are allowing your brain to completely unwire the old behaviours and wire in new ones. When still partly pursuing old behaviours, this rewiring process can become complicated if you are still using the old circuits but also trying to create new ones, leaving your brain uncertain as to which path it should take. Abstaining completely also has the benefit of allowing dopamine to fully reset, without the ongoing pursuit of behaviours that are pushing on the *pleasure* side of the dopamine seesaw, creating a deeper deficit that will then take longer to rebalance.

When you continue to use the eating disordered behaviours, even if in a reduced capacity, it's effectively the same as still taking your *drug* and getting a fix. Once your brain has sampled another taste of that *drug* of energy deficit, the brain circuits pursuing the addictive behaviours will spark into life, and your brain will then automatically try to pursue this further. The resulting dopamine response is also going to create powerful cravings for even more. This all makes it incredibly hard to engage in the behaviours in a reduced way.

The other risk with attempting to apply moderation to your behaviours, rather than completely giving them up, is that your brain can find clever ways to get the same level of *fix*, but it looks like reduced behaviour use. For example, you can convince yourself that you are eating a lot more food, but because you have decided to apply moderation to giving up restriction, it's left room for sneaky forms of restrictive eating to creep in. This can manifest as eating more frequently, but if you look at things more closely, you are eating less on each occasion, and over the whole day, there is very little difference to your intake. The same can happen with movement. Perhaps you decide to reduce walking to half the time it was each day. However, the walks simply become faster and more intense to still get that same dopamine *hit*.

And ultimately, let's face it, anyone who has tried to cut back on movement rather than stop it will know that as soon as you are out and engaging in the movement, it's much harder to stop yourself and come home. Not going at all can be the easier and more successful approach.

It's understandable, though, that some of you reading this are going to be of the mindset that giving everything up in one go is not something you are ready to do. Perhaps it feels too big a leap, too difficult emotionally, or you are still contemplating how willing you are to make changes. Therefore, there will be those of you for whom beginning the process with some smaller changes, which could be considered a moderation approach rather than full abstinence, is the preferred option.

If this is the case for you, some ideas are given below as to what moderation can look like in practice and how to manage the risks associated with it.

## Meal Plans

Perhaps the most common tool used in eating disorder treatment that prescribes moderation rather than abstinence from restrictive eating is a meal plan. It might be *prescribed* to you by an eating disorder treatment team or dietician, or maybe you have created your own.

Meal plans are essentially a prescription for food. They can advise what to eat, what times to eat and how much. People with eating disorders who have been given meal plans have in some cases been told not to eat above the plan (which takes away any ability to eat without restriction). Others are told that the plan is the minimum they need to eat, but the level of detail the plan provides is very restrictive when compared to the person's hunger and only exacerbates thoughts that their high appetite is *wrong* and should be suppressed. This has the effect of maintaining the brain circuits that pursue restrictive eating and pushes further onto the dopamine seesaw, driving cravings to restrict even more.

Overcoming an eating disorder takes self-empowerment and self-direction, albeit with support and reassurance. When you are handed a meal plan, a lot of the self-empowerment you might have had is removed. Meal plans are often compared to riding a bike with stabilisers (or training wheels). To me, they are more comparable to being the backseat passenger on a bike while someone else is riding it. It does very little to teach you how to ride the bike yourself.

Using a meal plan can be seen as a way to moderate restrictive eating and remove some of the restriction. However, most meal plans don't allow you to fully abstain from restrictive eating and find complete freedom with food and in this way will hinder your ability to fully overcome the restrictive eating disorder. But that does not mean meal plans cannot have a place in the process.

You might feel that you need this structured guidance to in-crease your eating in a more prescribed way. This can certainly also be of value if you are at risk of refeeding syndrome in the short term. Meal plans can also serve as a means of damage limitation if you are not ready to make more changes but need to maintain physical stability.

Meal plans should only be used in the short term, if at all, for those who are serious about fully overcoming an eating disorder. Meal plans prescribe moderation, and while rules and limits remain in place as to how much to eat, what and when, they will prevent you from ever developing the necessary skills to understand your body signals and trust your hunger.

## Exercise Reduction or Switching

When it comes to applying moderation to exercise or move-ment, you might work with a professional on an exercise reduc-tion program or attempt to create your own. The goal can be to reduce the amount of time you spend exercising each day or week, reducing the intensity or switching one type of exercise for another, e.g., swimming for yoga.

It's very likely that professionals who advocate this approach for people with restrictive eating disorders are unaware of just how highly addictive the exercise is. A lot of professionals who don't fully understand eating disorders might consider the only problem with a person exercising when they are attempting to overcome one is that it hinders their weight gain or causes them to lose more weight than is *healthy* for them.

Exercise reduction—or even exercise switching—does not ad-dress the root cause of the disorder, which is the brain's pow-erful addiction to the movement and pursuit of energy deficit. As with any addiction, to overcome it in the first instance, absti-nence is the gold standard approach. Someone who has a depen-dence on gambling or to alcohol rarely does well if they attempt from day one to *just cut back* on their usual consumption. The same is true for a person addicted to exercise or movement.

For all the reasons described above, in terms of what's hap-pening within your brain and what's needed to fully reprogram it, abstinence is always going to be the method with the lowest risk of failure. Chapter 5 discusses cross addictions and covers the risks that can arise from swapping one form of compulsive behaviour for another. In the case of exercise, this might be swapping running for walking.

Once again, though, for some of you, an attempt to moderate your exercise as a form of risk limitation or as a step towards full abstinence can have benefits. Any changes in terms of reduced engagement in the behaviours can be a positive step, and so, as with meal plans, you might decide that this method will be an initial part of your process to overcome the eating disorder.

### Moderation in Relation to Other Eating Disorder Behaviours

When it comes to the range of other compulsive behaviours that can make up an eating disorder, you might prefer to apply a moderation approach, or this may be the guidance you receive from a professional.

Examples of applying moderation to other behaviours include:

- **Purging through vomiting** – Of course to fully overcome the eating disorder, purging through vomiting needs to stop entirely. However, you might feel that stopping it all at once is too big a leap, and so you want to *toe dip* as a starting point. Applying a moderation approach to purging will involve creating very strict boundaries for yourself in terms of how often you will allow yourself to purge, hopefully with a significant reduction to now. You will then need to find barriers that will help prevent you from engaging in purging behaviours outside of these times to ensure that the behaviours do reduce and do not re-escalate.

- **Use of laxatives or diet pills** – As discussed previously, stopping these suddenly might be more harmful to your body from a medical perspective. Therefore, if you have a dependence on laxatives or other substances, it is worthwhile to seek medical support and advice on what you need to do to reduce them.

- **Weighing yourself** – Some people decide that they would like to continue to know their weight as they go through the process of overcoming the eating disorder, even if they are abstaining from all other behaviours in full. Carefully consider the benefits or potential harm knowing your weight will have in this process. If you decide you would like to continue to weigh yourself, then, as with other behaviours, set boundaries and find ways to keep to them. Create rules for yourself that you will only step on the scales once a fortnight or once a month (as examples) and that you will find ways to reduce temptation outside of these times.

- **Calorie counting** – For some people, obsessive calorie counting can be a significant part of the eating disorder and very addictive in nature. Abstaining from any numbers is recommended as you begin to abstain from restriction. However, if stopping suddenly seems too big a leap in one go, moderation might look like setting boundaries, such as only allowing yourself to count once a day or, if you usually write the numbers down, stopping this. If you do look at the numbers and compare two or more items to decide what to eat, have a rule that you must eat the one with the highest value, or ideally both.

- **Behaviours stemming from food obsession** – Food obsession is in part a natural response of your brain to being in a malnourished state. Your brain is guiding you towards food by making you notice, see and think about it in ways that become obsessive. However, over time, the more you engaged in these behaviours and the more reward your brain deemed from them, the more habitual they became. Overcoming these will in part occur naturally as you eat more and develop an energy-balanced body, but there will also be unwiring and rewiring work on these obsessions to do. Therefore, if you look at recipes frequently, follow *food porn* accounts on your social media feeds, or spend more time than an average person in the supermarkets, and you want to apply a moderation rather than abstinence approach, set more boundaries for yourself. For example, you will only look up recipes when you absolutely need to and no more than once a week. You will reduce the number of food porn accounts you follow and only scroll through social media for a certain amount of time a day. You will only allow yourself to visit the supermarket once or twice a week when you really need to buy items and then buy large amounts at once.

Overall, applying a moderation approach to the process of reprogramming your brain from an eating disorder will only take you so far. There are risks to this method, and it can make the process harder in the short and long term. With a moderation approach there is a risk of getting trapped in a life of moderation, still having to work hard to control your behaviours each day, which ultimately maintains a negative impact on your life. This is discussed in more detail in Chapter 12, where the topic of *quasi recovery* is covered.

At the end of the day, this is your process in overcoming a restrictive eating disorder—a process that you take ownership of. It might be that you need to toe dip into the process initially because diving in is too overwhelming and distressing. You may need to reassure yourself that changes are possible for you before you take that larger leap of faith. Perhaps there are medical issues that apply, and you need to apply moderation in the first couple of weeks of the process.

A period of full abstinence is always going to be preferable because it gives your brain the best chance to fully reprogram, hence leading to stronger overall success and with lower risk of lapses. Once in the abstinence process, most people find that it's easier than attempting to navigate the more confusing waters of behaviour reduction and moderation. Conversely to what you might think, in 99 percent* of cases, abstinence really is less distressing than moderation.

*This statistic is coming from my experiences and those that I've witnessed in others!*

· · · ● · ● · ● · · ·

# Let's Talk about Habits...
# Making and Breaking Them

Whether you apply an abstinence or moderation approach, the disordered thoughts, emotions and behaviours that arise from the eating disorder and addictive pursuit of energy deficit are now very entrenched and automatic habits that will be harder to stop and change than other habits in your life. To abstain from your addictive habits, or at least modify them, it can help to have more understanding about habits and steps to help you make and break them. After all, your goal is to ensure that you can remove your old habits, so they are effectively unwired and wire in new, positive ones.

At the beginning of the chapter, a neuroscience-based explanation of what habits are and what drives them was provided. Ultimately, your brain is very keen to habituate as many thoughts and behaviours as it can because it's more efficient and frees up space for other things. Therefore, any repeated exposure to a behaviour, thought or emotion will be noticed by your brain and wired in to make it easier to follow the same path in future with little conscious effort. And if high emotions are attached to the action you are wiring in, it will wire in even faster. In this section, information is provided about what's needed to make and break habits so that as you dive into the process to overcome the eating disorder, abstaining from old habits and forming new ones, you can do so with a greater chance of success. It's also important to remember that this success is dependent on you not only focusing on stopping the behaviours you no longer want but also ensuring you are replacing them with habits you do want.

## The Habit Loop

You might already be familiar with the habit loop or habit cycle. The same brain-based loop lies at the core of every habit we engage in and awareness of this can help when you are thinking about making and breaking habits.

**CUE-** A particular cue in your environment or your internal state, such as anxiety or stress, will tell your brain to seek the response that it recognises will bring instant gratification. As such, the cue automatically triggers your brain into the habit response.

**ROUTINE-** This is the behaviour you are trying to stop or to start doing and it stems from the cue. All habits need to be associated with a particular cue.

**REWARD-**This is the reward your brain receives that tells it that this loop is worth remembering and repeating. To embed a new habit, it's important to find ways to get a brain-based reward from it. Once your brain recognises that a particular behaviour will lead to a reward response, it will start firing in future before you start to engage in that behaviour, which then deepens your motivation to pursue it.

## Changing Habits

Changing any habits in life is an uphill battle against a brain that loves to follow habitual paths without conscious awareness. When you are trying to change habits related to an eating disorder, you will also face an additional layer of challenge from associated anxiety and fear-based reactions.

However, to have your best chance of breaking old habits and building new ones, it helps to be aware of each step in the habit loop and apply it.

### 1. IDENTIFY THE HABIT YOU WANT TO CHANGE

This might be a behaviour or emotional response.

### 2. RECOGNISE THE CUE/TRIGGER

What's happening at the time you are engaging in a habit that you want to stop? Where are you? What time is it? Who are you with? How are you feeling? Identify the trigger to the habit and you can then focus on creating a new response to form into a new and desired habit. It might be that the thought of being bigger, *I feel fat*, creeps into your mind or something external, such as tight clothing or comments from others create insecurity about your weight and size. Your habitual reaction might be to automatically restrict your food intake or engage in purging behaviours.

## 3. CHANGE THE RESPONSE

To change your automatic response to the trigger, you need to notice the trigger in the first instance and the thoughts it has generated so you can put in a new response. This takes self-awareness and focus. When you do try to stop yourself engaging in the old habit and engage in an alternative response, it will also feel very clunky and wrong because your brain has no wiring in that direction. Using the example of discomfort around your body size, you might change your response to practise positive thoughts about your body in that moment, such as, *I am curvaceous and beautiful*, and engage in an abstinence focused behaviour, such as sitting down to munch on a plate of cookies.

## 4. REWARD THE NEW RESPONSE

What's your motivation to make this change? This is where you dig deep. Notice any anxiety that has come up but stay with your new behaviours and praise yourself for your integrity, strength and courage. Wallow in pride in yourself, telling yourself that this is the best thing you can do for your future and even share your success with someone else. These responses will stimulate a reward response and will help further embed the new behaviour into your brain as it associates the new behaviour with a positive outcome.

## 5. REPEAT

Repetition is key for any habit change. Continue to identify triggers for old habits, replacing your habitual responses with new ones and rewarding the new behaviours. Then with each one, repeat and repeat and repeat.

People often say, *I've been sitting and eating for two days now, when does it get easier?*

This deep learning in your brain and habit change takes time. It can take weeks, months and for the most ingrained habits, years to really make and break them. Persistence and patience are needed. But over time, a new habit will form a new pathway in your brain in response to the trigger, which through ongoing repetition and reward becomes stronger than the pathway for the old habit. Soon enough, when you feel your clothes are tight or someone makes a comment about your size, your automatic response won't be to cut back on your food or go for a run. It will be to sit down with some cookies and enjoy a feeling of pride in yourself.

One final word of caution: the neural circuits of the old habit in your brain that was once so deeply embedded will still be lurking if you are not careful. Let it reactivate and it could quickly become strong again, so stay very vigilant.

**Identity Matters**

Identifying as the person who has already achieved your habit changing goal is another aspect to successful habit change that's often overlooked but can make the process more effective. Don't just consider yourself as being *in recovery* from the eating disorder but mentally connect to already being your future self who has overcome it in full and fabulous ways. This can then drive your successful behaviour change even further forward.

Mindset is a powerful thing. Consider yourself free of the eating disorder and it will make carrying out the behaviours and necessary habit changes that you would engage in naturally if you didn't have an eating disorder, more natural to engage in now too. Stay consistent and persistent with this and one day you won't have to pretend any longer because it will be real.

Developing new habits and behaviours takes repetition, determination, doggedness and, at times, a *feck it* attitude but it's definitely possible, even with the most entrenched and addictive habits in your life.

· · · ● ·● ● · ·

# Finding Your Inhibition & Engaging It

I explained earlier that with an eating disorder or any form of addiction, your ability to engage your PFC and apply inhibitory control to the addictive behaviours is reduced. However, to successfully overcome the eating disorder and abstain from or moderate the habits that are having such a destructive impact on your life, engaging the inhibitory control that is there is e ssential.In the morning, switch off your phone, stop working, avoid studying or anything else that will take your mental focus, to ensure that you stay focused on not going on your automatic walk today. And yes, overcoming an eating disorder does mean stopping a lot of other life distractions for a time but this is often necessary to give you the best chance to focus on making sure that you engage in the new and positive behaviours more consistently, so that they become automatic and give you the free future you are striving for

Your brain currently follows the neural pathways that form part of the overall eating disorder neural network automatically and habitually whenever it recognises a particular cue to do so. This could be a time of day, being in a particular environment or certain people. To take an alternative path to the one your brain is used to, means that you first need to inhibit the automatic response and then engage in the desired response instead. An example of this is that you get up at the same time each day and eat the same cereal in a very routine way. You want to change this habit and so you need to inhibit your natural urge to reach for the box of cereal and your usual bowl and instead push yourself towards the big, delicious breakfast you want to have. If your brain is distracted, even in a small way, then the inhibition of your habitual brain pathway will be forgotten. This is because the brain structures involved in inhibition are located in your PFC where attention, focus and alertness occur, and your brain can't consciously focus on more than one thing at a time. Keeping to your desired task and inhibiting your usual habits takes intense focus, especially when your ability for inhibitory control in relation to these eating disorder behaviours is already reduced in comparison to that which you can apply to other areas of your life.

But you do have the capacity for inhibitory control, even if it's reduced in relation to the eating disorder, and you use it all the time. You use it to stop yourself scrolling on your phone when you need to be working or studying; you use it when someone says something annoying to stop yourself from arguing because you know that arguing would be futile and you use it if you have an insect bite that's itching like mad, but you know you shouldn't scratch it.

Eating disorder or no eating disorder, you have an inhibitory control system that isn't broken. You just need to apply added focus to use it on your eating disordered habits.

## Applying Inhibition to Abstain from Eating Disorder Behaviours

To inhibit your habitual and routine disordered thoughts and behaviours, your first step is to remain focused on stopping the habits before they naturally kick in.

Manage any potential distractions that will interrupt your ability for inhibition before they take hold. If you don't do this, then before you know it you will find that you have gone down the usual disordered path because you were too distracted by answering a text to realise. Identify patterns in where distractions occur most commonly in your day and stop you from taking the path you had been determined to take. When you identify these common distractions, you can stop them before they start.

Where does your attention go when you are aiming to have that huge lunch and then find you have your usual safe lunch on your plate? When does the urge to be distracted from your eating disorder bashing intentions set in? Find these things, weed them out and address as many of them as possible.

Applying this to a practical example could be that you have set yourself the goal not to go for your habitual walk at lunch time. You have applied focus to deciding not to go and you feel committed. Late in the morning you receive a work call and following that you pick up a book to study. Before you realise what's happened, you are walking back in the front door, having been for your usual walk on autopilot as you were too distracted by other things to stop (or inhibit) yourself from going.

So, what do you do instead?

In the morning, switch off your phone, stop working, avoid studying or anything else that will take your mental focus, to ensure that you stay focused on not going on your automatic walk today. And yes, overcoming an eating disorder does mean stopping a lot of other life distractions for a time but this is often necessary to give you the best chance to focus on making sure that you engage in the new and positive behaviours more consistently, so that they become automatic and give you the free future you are striving for.

• • • ●•● •• •

# A Bit More Information About Deep Learning and Neuroplasticity

Before moving onto the next chapter, exploring all the things that make overcoming a restrictive eating disorder so hard, I want to conclude this one with a bit more information about neuroplasticity and what's required for the deep learning process as you reprogram your brain.

Neuroplasticity is the term used to describe the way in which your brain's circuits and networks change and reorganise in response to new learning and experiences. This ability of your brain to change is key in ensuring that the deep learning and rewiring needed to overcome an eating disorder are possible.

Connections between the neurons that are being used through your thoughts, actions and experiences in your day-to-day life are constantly being built and strengthened. At the same time, the connections between neurons that are no longer being used are reduced or removed entirely. In this way, neural networks will change depending on what you use. If you stop using a network altogether, for example through abstaining from an old habit or pattern of behaviours, then that network will begin to disintegrate and possibly, over time, disappear altogether. This is what you want to happen as you make and break habits to overcome the eating disorder.

The brains of babies, children and young adults are incredibly plastic and able to change very quickly as learning and growth occur. The level of plasticity your brain has does reduce with age, but your brain holds onto its neuroplastic abilities throughout your life span.

The neuroplastic abilities of your brain mean that brain changes are still possible, no matter how old you are, how long you have had an eating disorder or how entrenched you believe the behaviours to be. Neuroplasticity makes it possible for even those with the longest duration of eating disorder behaviours and deeply entrenched habits to reprogram their brain in the same way as anyone else.

*Neurons that Fire Together, Wire Together*

This is an often-cited quote by a famous neuroscientist, Donald Hebb. It underlies the basis of neuroplasticity, and the ability we humans have to change our brains through learning and experience.

Understanding more about neuroplasticity can enable you to use your brain's ability to adapt and rewire to your advantage as you abstain from the eating disorder's addictive habits and build behaviours that are not in pursuit of energy deficit.

## Thoughts, Experiences & Behaviours Change Brain Circuits

Changes to or strengthening of brain circuits occurs passively through behaviours, experiences and thoughts that you sub-consciously engage in each day. However, you can also actively pursue these things to deliberately affect the brain circuits that develop in order to generate brain circuits and networks that will work for you in your future.

The thoughts, experiences and actions that you engage in af-fect which of your brain cells fire together to form connections that when repeatedly fired will grow into stronger and more embedded *wired-in* networks.

If you repeat these thoughts, actions and behaviours over and again, the neurons will begin to fire automatically. This is when habits have been formed. The more deeply you embed pathways driving new thoughts and behaviours by repeatedly engaging in them, the faster your brain will use them automatically in future.

Your brain wants to apply neuroplasticity to guide your ac-tions and thoughts. Doing so uses less energy in terms of con-scious focus, which frees up energy and space to think about and pursue other things.

## Challenge – Repeat

When you understand the basic principles of neuroplasticity in this way, the saying that many in eating disorder communities will be familiar with—*challenge-repeat*—makes sense. *Challenge-repeat* relates to facing an eating disorder *challenge* as part of the process to overcome the eating disorder, but instead of just doing it once, you repeat it multiple times. As you do so, it becomes easier with each repetition.

What is happening in your brain as you go through this challenge–repeat process?

When you first face a new *challenge,* such as eating something new and less restrictive, there will be no or only very weak connections between the neurons involved in eating that food. It will feel clunky and wrong because your brain is being asked to fire in a new direction, and your brain prefers familiar and habitual paths. The more you repeat the *challenge,* the easier it becomes as the neural connections between the synapses involved in that eating behaviour have formed an increasing number of bonds that are also being strengthened. This path is then easier for your brain to recognise and pursue in future. With sufficient repetition, this new non–restrictive behaviour becomes more deeply embedded into your brain and will ultimately become a future habit. At this point you have used your brain's neuroplasticity to create habits allowing you to pursue a life beyond the eating disorder.

## Neuroplasticity Also Applies to Thoughts

It's not only actions and behaviours that can change through neuroplasticity. Thoughts and thinking patterns can also be changed.

Anyone with a restrictive eating disorder will have automatic disordered thoughts that are hard-wired into their brain. These thoughts act as triggers driving automatic engagement in the addictive behaviours either directly or because they first lead to an altered emotional state. This then triggers the behaviour. Thoughts can be changed through neuroplasticity and can make the process of abstaining from the behaviours a bit easier too.

Changing thoughts requires deliberate effort and needs to initially occur at a conscious level. You can deliberately choose to engage in thoughts that are positive towards the process of overcoming the eating disorder and towards your body and yourself. You can choose these thoughts, even if at first you don't believe them to be true. Repeatedly choose positive thoughts, engage in behaviours that align with these thoughts, and they will begin to wire into your brain circuitry so that with enough repetition, they become automatic.

A practical example of applying neuroplasticity to your thoughts is in relation to body image. People with restrictive eating disorders often have poor body image and automatic thoughts about their body that reflect this. To use neuroplasticity here, you need to notice when a negative body image thought enters your conscious awareness and replace it with a positive thought about your body. Don't forget that you don't have to believe the new thoughts at first. That will come later. Make a conscious effort to regularly apply kind thoughts towards your body and engage in behaviours that demonstrate an appreciation for it. Gradually, these body positive thoughts and behaviours will deepen into new brain circuits, and you become someone who is more body confident and appreciative of their physical form. This is not an overnight process, though. It takes ongoing conscious effort, but it will be worth it as you realise the freedoms and confidence it brings to you.

## Apply Positive Emotion

Your brain also learns faster when there are emotions behind a new experience or pattern of thinking.

Your brain is naturally wired to always be on the lookout for danger. This is a basic survival mechanism but not always a helpful one as it does make us prone to negativity. It also means that your brain learns new things incredibly quickly when negative emotions are behind an experience compared to neutral or positive emotions. Despite this, applying positive emotions to the new behaviours that you want your brain to learn at a deep level will help it to understand that this new and unfamiliar thing it's encountering is positive, worth remembering and repeating. The more positive emotion you can apply to the new behaviours as you abstain from the eating disorder, the faster your brain will strengthen connections between the necessary neurons that will form non-eating disordered circuits and embed them in.

It's very difficult to apply positive emotions to new behaviours that feel deeply wrong. You will need to apply conscious effort to make yourself feel positive, attempting to generate feelings of excitement and joy about the process as you go through it, using the things you want from your future life to motivate you.

## What Else Promotes Neuroplasticity?

Three other key factors make it more likely that you will develop strong connections between the synapses of the neurons needed to create the necessary brain networks for your free future. These are focus and attention, a bit of stress and then a period of rest. It becomes clear why these factors are important when you understand what's happening in your brain at a chemical level.

When you apply focus and attention to the things you want to learn or change, the neurons release a chemical called acetylcholine. This puts an attentional spotlight on the new learning and the neurons involved, which your brain notices.

The addition of a little bit of stress and anxiety as you go through the brain reprogramming process is actually a good thing, as long as you use that stress in a positive direction. Now, let's be real, as you go through the process of overcoming an eating disorder, you are going to have times of feeling stressed and anxious. Keep your focus on the positive new behaviours you are developing; the adrenaline your brain will be releasing as a result of that stress response can help. Adrenaline increases your alertness and vigilance to what you are doing, which also promotes neuroplasticity.

A practical example might be aiming to eat a whole pizza for lunch. At the time that you are focused on this new behaviour and eating that pizza, acetylcholine and adrenaline will be released in your brain and will mark the neurons that need to form connections for the desired *eating pizza at lunchtime* brain pathways to develop. The actual changes to the neurons, in terms of their forming connections to one another, happens later. It's when your brain is in a state of deep relaxation, such as sleep, that other brain chemicals recognise the marked neurons and wire in synaptic connections between them. This makes them more likely to fire together in future.

The deep relaxation state required for this can be actual sleep or a period of deep brain rest through meditation, deep relaxation or daydreaming.

To sum up the pizza eating example, you need focus and attention on eating and enjoying the pizza at lunchtime; allow yourself to feel a bit agitated, confused and stressed by the experience but stay with it. After the experience, do some meditation or ensure a good night's sleep that night. Repeat this consistently, and in no time, eating pizza at lunchtime will be a brain circuit that your brain follows with ease.

## Final Points on Neuroplasticity

One of the key things to understand, especially for those of you who are older and who have had an eating disorder for decades, is that research has repeatedly now demonstrated that your brain holds onto its ability to learn new things and rewire throughout the life span. Therefore, it's never too late for you to change the wiring of your brain—away from the eating disordered brain circuits that have dominated your life and towards a non-eating disordered future.

The next point is that neuroplasticity does not feel good when it's happening. This applies to anything new that is hard to learn, which could be learning to play a piano, speak Japanese or overcome an eating disorder. It will feel uncomfortable, frustrating and very wrong at times because it's unfamiliar territory to your brain. Expect the process to be hard and for it not to feel right. Understand that it will demand a lot of conscious focus and effort, and it can create agitation, with ongoing feelings of brain fog.

The process of neuroplasticity also needs to be self-directed. Your brain chemicals and changes needed will not work their magic if someone else *does recovery* to you. It's not possible to force neural rewiring on another person. Your brain learns when it's really engaged in the process, so you need to be in the driving seat of directing your own journey to overcome the

eating disorder. This relates to the importance of self-empowerment, which is discussed in Chapter 6.

Rewiring also takes time. It does not happen in an instant. Repetition, diversity and rich new experiences all make
rewiring much more likely to succeed.

Persist and stay committed to the process, and the new connections that you want in the brain networks you need to develop
will form and embed. As this happens, the thoughts, behaviours
and habits that are positively free of the eating disorder and
its addictions and compulsions will become embedded into and
deeply learnt by your brain. This will then leave the old brain
networks that drove the eating disorder unused, and over time
they will be broken down and trampled on by your new, positive
brain wiring.

---

1. Whitelaw M, Gilbertson H, Lam PY, Sawyer SM. Does ag-
gressive refeeding in hospitalized adolescents with anorexia
nervosa result in increased hypophosphatemia? J Adolesc
Health. 2010 Jun; 46(6):577–82. doi: 10.1016/j.jadohealth.2
009.11.207. Epub 2010 Jan 25. PMID: 20472215.

# Chapter Five

---

# What Makes an Eating Disorder So Hard to Overcome?

B eyond the brain-based models that have already been explained in relation to addictions and why they are so powerful, there are several other important neurobiological and social factors that add to the difficulty of overcoming addictive and eating disorders. Some of the most common are covered in this chapter. Understanding these will make you more likely to recognise when they are impacting your progress, what's happening and why. They say that knowledge is power, and although it still won't be easy, you can use this understanding to protect against these potential obstacles and put measures in place to manage them.

• • • • ● • ● • • •

# Triggers

In our current culture, the word *trigger* is thrown around a lot. People feeling *triggered,* something *triggering* them or accusing someone else of being a *trigger.* By no means is this only in relation to eating disorders, but it's a way of speaking that has seemingly become fashionable.

The term *trigger* is also used widely in eating disorder recovery communities. People often speak about *triggers* in relation to an occurrence, a situation, place, person or something that's been said. They attribute this to why they then experienced a stronger urge to engage in the eating disordered behaviours.

When it comes to addictions, the term *trigger* is also commonly used and in the same context. Something has pushed the person with the addiction into using their *drug.*

It's important to be aware of triggers when you are overcoming an eating disorder as they can be real and powerful. But we should be careful of how freely the word is used outside of its true meaning, as this results in a risk of genuine and potentially harmful triggers being trivialised.

**What are *triggers* in relation to addictive disorders?**

Triggers or cues can be anything that pushes your brain into automatically following the habitual network that drives your addictive behaviours and the related cascade of rituals, thoughts and emotions.

**What's happening inside your brain to make you more likely to engage in the addictive behaviours when you have met with a trigger?**

When your brain's reward system is activated by the addictive behaviour, it not only creates pleasurable feelings; it also causes changes in the way you respond to stimuli associated with that behaviour. Your brain associates the things present when you are engaging in the behaviour with the rewarding effects from it. Over time, these stimuli can be enough on their own to push your reward system into action and create intense feelings of wanting to engage in the addictive behaviour in that moment. In this way, the stimuli directly create strong cravings, and so we commonly refer to them as *triggers*.

A trigger can be anything that reminds you of your *drug*. This might be a situation, place, person, emotional state, a time of day or a memory. Just seeing or noticing this trigger makes your brain release a trickle of dopamine into the striatum, which focuses your attention back onto the goal of the addictive behaviour and produces a more intense feeling of attraction towards it. Even if you manage to resist resorting to the addiction at this point, what do we now know about the impact of the dopamine seesaw effect in the brain when it's had this rise above baseline? Dopamine levels will come back down again but to a level that's below baseline, stimulating the pain side of the dopamine balance. This swing to the dopamine deficit state produces a physiological response within you that's often referred to as craving. The craving then creates obsessive thoughts about wanting or needing to use your *drug* or behaviours. In the case of restrictive eating disorders, this can be circling and obsessive thoughts such as *How can I restrict at the next snack?* or *When can I purge and how can I do so without others noticing?* or *When will I be able to fit in more exercise?* These all-consuming thoughts are your brain's response to the physiological state of craving for its next hit of energy deficit.

This state of craving can become so uncomfortable that it will drive you to seek out your next dopamine hit by engaging in the addiction again—because this is the only way you know to make yourself feel better.

People who have overcome an addictive or eating disorder and been free of it for some time can remain vulnerable to strong triggers in their past. Encountering triggers that remind their brain of the previous addiction can remain very powerful. Meeting an old cue can cause a cascade of dopamine to enter the striatum, which results in a powerful lure back to the old addictive habits. For this reason, avoiding previously powerful triggers in the long term is recommended wherever possible. After all, why risk it?

**Triggers and Overcoming an Eating Disorder**

Applying the above information to a practical example, let's say that you are in the process of overcoming an eating disorder and you see a loved one putting on their running shoes, ready to go out for a run. Seeing this reminds you of running, which was a part of your exercise compulsion within the eating disorder. This reminder alone creates a small release of dopamine into your brain, taking your dopamine levels above baseline, making the idea of going for a run in that moment much more attractive. Even if you resist this, your dopamine seesaw will quickly swing back in the opposite direction, so you experience a dopamine deficit. This will leave you feeling anxious, agitated, restless and irritable. These symptoms of craving result in an even greater feeling of desperation to put on your own trainers and go for a run because your brain understands this to be the most powerful way to make you feel calm again.

When you understand what's happening inside your brain in relation to dopamine in this way, you can also appreciate why, as you overcome an eating disorder, any engagement in old behaviours can very quickly escalate. Restricting in terms of not having butter on your bread today might seem innocent enough when you are eating well otherwise. However, the small dopamine hit that comes from that restrictive behaviour will ultimately create a dopamine dip, creating symptoms of withdrawal and powerful urges to restrict more at the next meal or snack.

Triggers are a huge potential obstacle in the process of overcoming an eating disorder. Understanding why they are so powerful can help, and putting measures in place to trigger-proof your life and environment, especially in those early, fragile months, can make or break your success. Later, even as you feel stronger in the process, remain conscious that something that was a powerful trigger to your eating disorder behaviours in the past could still have an impact on you into your future.

• • • • • • • • • •

# Self-Identity

When you've had an eating disorder for any length of time, you develop deeply embedded brain circuits driving the addictive behaviours. At the same time there is *pruning* in your brain of circuits that drive behaviours and thought pathways you are no longer using. This results in the strongest brain pathways in your brain relating to the pursuit of your *drug* of energy deficit. Once this has occurred, your primary thoughts and feelings will relate to the addiction and how to pursue it. Therefore, it's only natural that this has an impact on your personality and on your self-identity.

When you develop an eating disorder, it's not uncommon to find that you lose your previous sense of identity and develop an identity related to it. You might even have started to label yourself as *anorexic, bulimic* or perhaps in relation to a strong behaviour that is driven by the eating disorder, for example as a *runner.*

Some people who have entrenched eating disorders have developed their careers around the behaviours in such a way that it drives a stronger identity and sense of self around their compulsions. For example, people with a strong exercise compulsion can go into jobs in the fitness world, perhaps as a personal trainer. Some pursue professional sports. These career choices allow them to engage in those very addictive and damaging behaviours in a manner that appears applaudable. Restrictive eating disorders can also naturally make people food obsessed because of their ongoing state of semi-starvation; some people enter jobs in nutrition or choose to work with food as chefs or in bakeries. This drives an identity towards one that is food focused, teaching others how to eat or feeding others, while eating restrictively and in very disordered ways themselves.

Another way in which you might have created a greater sense of identity around the eating disorder is from the social groups or communities you belong to. It might be that you move in social circles with people who are all into a certain sports pursuit, such as running. If the people you spend time with go out running every day, and this forms much of your conversation and how you spend time together, it can promote a strong running identity—despite the fact that for you running is a compulsive habit arising from the eating disorder.

Other forms of community that can have an impact on your self-identity with an eating disorder are those set up to support people with eating disorders. Peer support groups can be invaluable to people who are attempting to overcome an eating disorder, offering support from others who are going through the same or those who have been there. However, they can also strengthen your sense of identity as *eating disordered*. If these groups become strong forms of social connection, it can then be hard, if you are otherwise quite isolated, to want to move away from them. In some cases, this can result in these groups having the opposite effect to that intended, making it harder for you to give up a self-identity that holds onto the eating disorder.

Self-identity is powerful, and when you identify as something in this way, it can become a self-fulfilling prophecy. If you do self-identify as *anorexic* or *eating disordered*, it can make you feel resigned to your fate, believing that it's impossible for you to change. If you self-identify in this way for long enough, you may not be able to envision or believe in any alternative identity for yourself.

The medical model of treating addictions and eating disorders can exacerbate this issue of self-identity as it can disempower people. When you are given a label as the *patient*, it can leave you feeling disempowered when it comes to owning your recovery. Being treated as the *anorexic patient* can make you much less trusting in your own abilities to overcome the addictive behaviours. This leaves you believing that you must follow instructions, rather than creating your own future goals and aspiring to achieve them on your own terms. I'm not making this point to deter you from entering treatment if that is what you need to do, but if you do enter treatment, it's important that you hold on to a sense of your own identity beyond the role of a patient or someone with an eating disorder.

### How Do You Address Your Self-Identity?

Firstly, remember you are not the eating disorder, you are not the addiction and you are not the behaviours you engage in, no matter how compulsively.

Recognise that the eating disorder is giving you a life you do not want as part of your future. Identify all the ways the eating disorder and the addictive behaviours related to it are ruining your life, and take ownership of the fact that you want things to be different. Tell yourself that those behaviours and the eating disorder driving them are not who you are, and they will not be part of your future life.

Build a desire to pursue new goals or perhaps to rediscover old goals and focus on these, using them to help formulate who you are and who you can be. Believe in your ability to achieve those goals and begin to move towards them.

Perhaps you refer to *my eating disorder* when you talk about it, or when other people talk to you about *your eating disorder.* This implies that the eating disorder is a part of you. It can help to begin to think of the eating disorder as something that's detached from you. Refer to it as *the eating disorder.* It's not something you have or want ownership of, and just that change in how you think about it and refer to it can be a powerful way to disassociate from it.

Likewise, when you notice yourself identifying as the person with the eating disorder or even as *the bulimic,* or any other labels you might attach in that regard, stop and say to yourself, *That is not who I am now.* Then continue to move towards your future with the belief that you have the self-control to overcome these addictive behaviours and have the future that you are starting to build.

During this process of shaking off the old eating disorder identity and building yourself a new and empowering one, it's likely that for a time you will feel something of an identity crisis. This is when you lose what you have known and grapple to find who you are becoming. It can feel as if you enter a limbo land for a time. Stay with it and as you progress, you will build a new sense of who you are. This will be made up of parts of who you used to be before the eating disorder, but with the strength, resilience, knowledge and wisdom gained from having lived with it and the process of overcoming it.

• • • ● ● • ● ● • •

# Thought Patterns and Self-Talk

With an eating disorder, you not only develop habits in terms of behaviours, but your thought patterns and self-talk also become habitual. These can then also act as triggers or cues for the compulsive behaviours.

Examples of this are:

- *I will eat my usual amount of food now but make up for it later.*

- *I have tried recovery before, and it never works, so I know I can't overcome this and might as well not bother trying.*

- *If my partner was more supportive, I could eat more, but as they aren't, I can't.*

- *I won't buy that cake now because I know that I have food at home to use up* (which of course is more restrictive).

If you have a restrictive eating disorder, you probably recognise some of these patterns and can identify others that are typical for you.

These thoughts are your brain's attempt to justify continuing to engage in the behaviours. Very often the same thoughts will occur daily as your brain has learnt patterns of thinking that will automatically lead you further into the eating disordered circuits, resulting in the *fix* it craves.

Habitual thought patterns can also have emotions attached to them. For example, in the case of the thought about the unsupportive family member, the emotions of resentment, frustration and sadness can be present. Your brain then further identifies these as an emotional state that the eating disorder behaviours will help to soothe.

It's impossible to abstain from your thoughts when they arise automatically. However, when you're going through the process of overcoming the eating disorder, be very mindful of the thoughts popping into your head and where they are leading you.

The more you can develop new thoughts that lead to abstinence behaviours and regularly repeat them to yourself, the more likely you will be able to unwire the old thought patterns and wire in these new ones. Over time these new positive thoughts will become cues for the new behaviours.

## Negative Self-Talk and Beliefs

Other complicating factors to overcoming an eating disorder are negative self-talk and beliefs. Not everyone finds these problematic, although everyone experiences negative self-talk at times, even people with generally good self-confidence or self-esteem. For some, though, negative self-talk is strongly habitual. It's a way of life, comparable to having a bully living inside their head. Take time to reflect on whether this applies to you and, if so, what impact it has on the eating disorder behaviours.

Being prone to negative self-talk and high anxiety can arise from your upbringing or life history in addition to your genetic blueprint. People susceptible to this are likely to have learnt early in the development of the eating disorder that the dopamine release from it enabled them to feel calmer or uplifted. If they had been reliant on seeking approval or reassurance from others before for how they were feeling internally, this need was reduced when they found the natural feel-good state that engaging in the eating disorder gave them. Therefore, for some, negative self-talk—or a history of anxiety, high stress or trauma—would have been a strong factor in the development of their dependence on the eating disorder.

When you speak critically to yourself often enough, with attached emotions and behaviour to support the thoughts, it will lead to associated beliefs about yourself. This will then impact your attempts to abstain from the eating disorder behaviours. For example, you might tell yourself you are not worthy or deserving of nice food. Telling yourself this often enough while avoiding good things has led to a belief that then becomes a strong cue, triggering your brain into behaviours of food avoidance and restriction.

Overcoming negative thoughts and beliefs is incredibly hard. Just as the eating disorder behaviours are strongly habitual and you largely engage in them without preceding conscious awareness, so, too, are your thoughts. That is not to say that you cannot change your thinking habits. You can and to overcome the eating disorder, it's a crucial part of the process.

Your brain unwires old habits and wires in new learning through experiences and emotions. Thoughts or words alone are said to have very little impact on deep learning within the brain. It's ultimately the emotions behind the thoughts that will make your brain pay attention to them. Some people will recommend using affirmations to change negative self-talk and instil more positive thoughts and beliefs about yourself. The topic of affirmations is covered in the accompanying handbook. Affirmations have some benefits, but for them to work, you will need to ensure that you are attaching positive emotions to the words you use.

When you notice a negative automatic thought, recognise it and change it to something positive. It's also very important not to berate yourself for having these negative thoughts, even when they are persisting. Don't judge yourself that the thoughts are there; just be mindful of them, notice what might have triggered them and then attempt to reframe them.

Perhaps you've had a thought that your thighs are fat or that you are lazy and undeserving. Recognise that these thoughts are there and reframe them, talking back to yourself, ideally out loud.

*My thighs are bigger than they once were, but that is to be expected. I am overcoming an eating disorder, and weight gain is part of that process. I am not lazy. I am working hard to overcome a powerful addictive disorder, and I need to apply myself fully to resting and eating in a process that creates difficult emotions but will allow my brain to reprogram so I fully heal.*

Avoid ruminating on the past and old mistakes and instead consider what you have learnt and how this will serve you in your future.

It's likely that negative self-talk has been a cue for engaging in the eating disorder behaviours for years. When you do find yourself lost in a spiral of negative thoughts and feel compelled to restrict or compensate, recognise why you are feeling these urges and immediately recommit to your decision to abstain from the eating disorder by eating something, sitting down and not compensating.

Negative self-talk can become a spiral. Instead, develop and nurture the skill of being self-aware of your thoughts.

The eating disordered thought patterns and negative self-talk and beliefs have been wired into your brain as a form of deep learning. Your brain created these circuits because at some point in your past, these thoughts and beliefs served you by rewarding you or keeping you safe. These thoughts and beliefs can be changed through unwiring and wiring in new ones, just as the eating disordered habits can be changed. It takes time, focus and persistence, but it is possible.

• • • ● • ● • • •

## Multiple Addictive Behaviours

With a restrictive eating disorder, you can develop multiple addictive or compulsive behaviours. This can be a complicating factor when it comes to addressing the eating disorder and making the necessary behavioural and habit changes.

When someone is addicted to multiple substances or behaviours, it is known as *poly-pharmacy*addiction. With poly-pharmacy addiction, abstaining from one of the behaviours can very often cause an increase in the use of another. It's easy to understand why this would happen. You are no longer pushing up your dopamine and numbing your inner pain from the use of multiple *drugs*, so the *drug* you do continue to use is needed at a higher level to get the same effects as when you were using both. A non-eating-disorder-related example of this is someone who has a dependence on smoking and gambling. They stop gambling, but this results in them smoking more.

The consequence of poly-pharmacy addiction and continuing to use one *drug*, even though another has been stopped, is that it does not allow for your brain to restore its dopamine levels to an equilibrium because behaviours driving dopamine up are still being pursued. Therefore, the overall dopamine deficit is also becoming deeper.

Unfortunately, with multiple addictions, people often fail to recognise that it's even an issue. They might think, *I don't have a problem with drinking because I don't drink every day,* but on the days they don't drink, they are gambling more. Perhaps then on the days they are not gambling, they are Internet gaming. When they do stop and look at their week, it's easy to see that each day there is something that is giving them a dopamine *fix.*

This is also commonly seen in people with restrictive eating disorders. You might say, *I don't have an issue with exercise or movement as I only exercise three times a week,* but on the days you are not exercising, you are purging by vomiting or eating less. Perhaps, *I don't restrict every day,* but on the days you are not restricting as intensely, you are moving around more and/or purging through other methods. In this way, it's very easy to deny how big a problem the eating disorder is. Facing reality and addressing it necessitate a difficult and painful process.

When you are overcoming a restrictive eating disorder, it's vital to be aware of the issues that arise from having multiple addictive behaviours. People often begin to eat with much less restriction but choose not to simultaneously address their movement compulsions, even negotiating that they will allow themselves to continue that habitual walk or run but *eat more to make up for it.* This only results in movement compulsions becoming stronger. No longer getting the addictive effects from restriction leads their brain to seek out the next best approach it knows for a quick *fix,* which in this scenario is movement.

With a restrictive eating disorder, it's very likely that you have multiple compulsive and addictive behaviours. It's not always easy to identify them all until you stop and fully reflect on your day-to-day habits.

The best approach to address multiple addictive behaviours is to abstain from all of them at the same time. This gives your brain the best chance to restore dopamine homeostasis and reduces the risk of failing to make progress or sliding backwards in your pursuit of freedom.

When you consider the way in which your brain's circuitry has altered in response to the multiple addictive behaviours that make up the eating disorder, stopping all of them simultaneously also makes sense.

With the eating disorder, the circuits relating to pursuing the different addictive behaviours have become more deeply embedded in your brain, but there will also be connections between the circuits for each behaviour, forming a strong network of brain wiring. When you developed patterns such as, *If I eat more food, I will purge to compensate*, it led to the brain circuits driving restriction and purging to connect. When you looked at calories, habitually counting or tracking them, eating according to what the numbers said, it linked the calorie-counting circuit with that driving restrictive eating. When you jumped on the scales in the morning, didn't like what the numbers said and so went for a longer run that day, you linked the circuit for compulsive exercise with that of weighing yourself and body checking. I'm sure you get the point.

Therefore, if you are trying to stop running but continue to weigh yourself every day, every time you step on the scales in the morning, your brain circuits for running will light up, and your brain will then try to automatically push you in that direction. And the act of weighing yourself will have given rise to a small dose of dopamine, which we know is a powerful factor in driving the pursuit of more addictive behaviours. When you have worked extremely hard to suppress urges to exercise each time your brain tried to compel you in that direction, the last thing you need is something else to trigger an even stronger urge, which then takes even more effort to resist.

To overcome an eating disorder in full, the best method is to establish your unique cocktail of addictive behaviours and abstain from them altogether. Sometimes it's easier to say no to everything than to continue to pursue some. Of course, though, you are in charge of your process to overcome the eating disorder, and so you ultimately make those decisions. You might choose to stop certain behaviours entirely but still allow yourself to engage in others. If this is the case, as you are stopping the behaviours that you have chosen to address, remain very mindful that the behaviours you will allow yourself to engage in don't become more intense.

A final way in which your brain will try to find hits of dopamine when its persistent attempts to drive you to pursue the eating disordered behaviours keep failing is through your other addictive habits that up until now have been less rewarding and not as hotly pursued. It's worth also being mindful of this risk. Examples of this are things like social media use, which many people today have some form of addiction to, or keeping busy with work and studies, which is an issue discussed in more depth at the end of this chapter. You do not need to fully abstain from these other habits, but be self-aware of how often you engage in them and whether you are finding them more compelling.

• • • ● • ● • • ••

# Cross Addiction

The last section covered multiple or poly-pharmacy addictions, which is when you have more than one addictive behaviour or drug.

Cross addiction refers to when you are trying to overcome one addiction, but in doing so, you develop an addiction to a *drug* that is entirely new to you.

If you have used eating disordered behaviours as a powerful means to numb underlying symptoms of anxiety, depression or even past trauma, and you abstain from these, there is a risk you will develop a cross addiction. Abstaining from the addictive numbing behaviours results in deeply emotional withdrawal symptoms that are extremely uncomfortable and painful. When this happens, your brain can attempt to protect you from these negative feelings. If its attempts to pursue the old addictive behaviours and dopamine fix fail, it will seek alternative methods. Your brain then searches for other behaviours or substances that will create a rise in dopamine and its numbing effects.

For example, people who are abstaining from an addiction such as gambling might find that they drink more alcohol when the painful withdrawal symptoms start, putting them at risk of replacing a gambling disorder with alcohol dependence. Someone who is giving up alcohol might start smoking, even though they never have before.

This is a risk in eating disorder recovery too. The withdrawal symptoms, which can include anxiety, low mood, agitation, irritability or anger, can become intense and hard to sit with. Therefore, you can find yourself looking for other ways to feel better. This search is very often at a subconscious level.

With eating disorders, there are two types of risk in relation to cross-addictions.

### Cross Addiction to New Eating Disorder Behaviours

You might successfully abstain from the eating disorder behaviours that you have always engaged in, perhaps restrictive eating and purging through vomiting. However, as you move through the process of giving up these behaviours, you realise that you have started to exercise more, and this is becoming compulsive when it wasn't before. You have also developed body-checking behaviours that you didn't have previously but which are becoming increasingly habitual and compelling. This is when you abstain from old behaviours related to the eating disorder but develop a cross addiction or transference to new behaviours that also relate to it.

It's possible to understand how this comes about. Restrictive eating disorders are ultimately an addiction to the state of energy deficit, so when you stop using one set of behaviours to achieve this *fix*, your brain leads you to a different set of behaviours to get the same rewards it seeks.

This risk of cross addictions is another argument for abstaining from any behaviours that fall under a restrictive eating disorder umbrella, whether you have engaged in them before or not.

## Cross Addiction to Non-Eating-Disorder-Related Behaviours

It's also possible to develop a cross addiction to things that don't fall within an eating disorder. You might start to smoke as you go through the process to overcome the eating disorder or develop a compulsion for Internet gaming to numb and distract yourself.

A common cross addiction that I've seen in several clients is that as they abstain from the eating disorder behaviours, they develop behaviours that would typically be considered under the label of obsessive-compulsive disorder (OCD). The types of behaviours people develop are compulsive and very much anxiety driven, such as handwashing, checking light switches, tapping or other repetitive and disabling behaviours common to people with an OCD diagnosis. In some cases, the person has never had OCD behaviours before, and these first start as they abstain from their usual eating disorder behaviours. In others, there has been a previous history of OCD, but the OCD behaviours are largely controlled when the person is still deeply engaged in the eating disorder. However, the OCD behaviours significantly worsen when the person abstains from the eating disorder's compulsive behaviours. Although the links between OCD and eating disorders are still not fully understood, recent studies have found that up to 40 percent of people who have an eating disorder can develop a form of OCD within their lifetime[1].

Cross addiction is a real risk in overcoming any addiction and so, too, in overcoming a restrictive eating disorder. However, when you swap one addiction for another, your inner pain, which has been a factor in maintaining the original eating or addictive disorder, doesn't get addressed. This stops you from being able to fully find freedom and a non-addicted life.

It's important to remain aware of the risk of cross addiction as you work to overcome an eating disorder. Awareness alone can be a powerful means to prevent it. It will be crucial to develop tools that will enable you to sit through painful emotions, withdrawal symptoms and urges to re-engage in the addictive behaviours. You will possibly need to seek support from a coach or another professional to help you with this.

• • • • ● • ● • ● • •

# Ego Fatigue

Ego fatigue is a concept you need to be aware of as you go through the process to overcome an eating disorder. Anyone who has attempted to conquer any form of addictive disorder will recognise the impact ego fatigue can have.

Ego fatigue is the term used to describe the increasing strain that resisting compulsive urges creates. With it, you become mentally worn out. Your brain isn't designed to be constantly resisting impulses pulling you to things that it deems are pleasurable or even essential to survival.

The ongoing suppression of impulses leads to exhaustion and can result in relapse. When the addictive behaviours are so readily available, constantly resisting them and having to tell yourself *No, don't engage,* quickly becomes mentally draining.

You say to yourself, *No, I won't restrict; I won't purge; I won't move around the house just for the sake of it.* But then the thoughts come. *Well...maybe I won't have ice cream with the apple pie,* or, *If I do purge tonight, it will definitely be the last time.* As soon as these mental negotiations set in, it becomes almost inevitable that ego fatigue is about to tip you back to the eating disordered behaviours.

And when ego fatigue has set in and your determination to stay *in recovery* has faltered, it can initially be a relief to go back to the addictive behaviours. It can make you feel like you are free falling and create feelings of elation as you don't have to keep up the mental fight.

## How Do You Address Ego Fatigue?

Saying no repeatedly to addictive urges is exhausting and doesn't work. In fact, repeatedly saying no to yourself is more likely to make ego fatigue worse.

Imagine a small child who is misbehaving and doing something you don't want them to do. Repeatedly saying no to them rarely works. They are likely to ignore you and keep deliberately provoking. Instead, if you stop saying, *No,* and say, *Hey, what you are doing over there is boring; that's no fun... Come and have a look over here. Let's do this, which is really fun!* it might just get a better result and be a less exhausting and frustrating process.

How do you relate this to ego fatigue and the eating disorder's urges?

Reframe the situation in your mind. Look away from the temptation and tell yourself why you don't want to engage in the addictive behaviours, rather than just saying *No* to them. This might look like saying to yourself, *Apple pie is so much more delicious with ice cream, and that's what I really want to have.* Or *I am tired and don't enjoy walking the streets on my own; the couch looks far more inviting.* Or *I would be so upset if my child ever saw me purging, so I'm not going to risk it today.*

People who believe in their own abilities to control the urges luring them back to the addiction are also less likely to experience the depleting effects of ego fatigue. This is perhaps because if you don't believe you can control your impulses, you not only have to mentally fight to control them but also to override your belief that you can. Therefore, practising some level of belief in your own abilities can be an additional step to take to reduce the effects of ego fatigue. Using a coach or therapist to help with this could be of benefit.

The other important factor known to help with ego fatigue relates to your inner motivation to push against the impulses. If you are making changes to purely please others, you are much more likely to be affected by ego fatigue than if you have your own powerful inner reasons to push forward. Keep reminding yourself *why* you want to overcome the eating disorder. Make sure your *why* is emotionally powerful and motivating to you.

At the end of the day, there will be times (perhaps many times as those urges can come several times an hour, let alone multiple times a day) that you will need to just say *No!* to yourself. When you do, consider the voice you use in your inner dialogue. It's easy to get frustrated and angry with yourself, call yourself names for being tempted to go back to old behaviours and be punitive with yourself. However, this can add to feelings of despair or shame or leave you feeling punished. Instead, talk to yourself with a supportive voice. Be an ally to yourself and be a team in that internal dialogue. Say, *Let's not do that; let's do this instead. We don't really want to do that; it's not really what we want,* and allow yourself to feel supported and encouraged. It might sound daft, but sometimes these things can be the difference between continuing to abstain from the addictive behaviours or going back to them.

• • • ● • ● • • •

# The NOW Appeal

*Now appeal* is a powerful driving force in any addictive disorder. This is the tendency, when it comes to the addiction, to pursue immediate rewards rather than consider longer-term benefits that could arise from taking a different course of action.

The *now appeal* arises in large part because of our old friend dopamine. Dopamine will focus your attention very narrowly on your immediate goal with an urgent pull towards it. As dopamine is slowly released in pursuit of the goal, which in this case is the pursuit of energy deficit, you will experience cravings for more that are very hard to resist. When in a state of craving, your brain becomes much less able to consider anything other than immediate rewards. This is termed *delay discounting*, where immediate reward—which with an eating disorder might be feeling less anxious or depressed—has more value than long-term rewards. The consequence of the *now appeal* is that you respond to the craving because it feels more worthwhile in that moment than any imagined future happiness.

When someone is in pursuit of non-addictive goals, their prefrontal cortex (PFC) usually controls the *now appeal* and will override it. However, with an addiction, the PFC goes *offline,* and so the ability in that moment to consider the future is lost. There are three reasons for this:

1. The drive to pursue the addictive behaviour is so strong.

2. The reward from the behaviour is powerful, usually because the pain from abstaining has become too intense.

3. Pursuing the addictive behaviour is now a hardwired habit. This goes all the way down to being a habit of thinking above anything else, *How do I meet my fix of energy deficit today?*

This all culminates in your being trapped in the present moment, unable to think about the future. When you're responding to the eating disorder's urges, the future no longer makes sense.

When I reflect on my experience of living with an eating disorder, I can vividly recall the lure of the *now appeal*. I might have decided I would pursue behaviours that day that were abstaining from the eating disorder. I'd eat more, I wouldn't engage in any exercise and I would feel committed to these promises. Then the time of day I'd normally go for a compulsive and habitual walk would arrive. At first I would say to myself, *I'm not going, I'll stay in*, but within minutes I'd be feeling agitated, anxious, irritable and unable to think straight. Of course, these are all symptoms I now understand to be common to withdrawal from an addictive behaviour and cravings to engage in it. By this point, I could no longer remember why I'd decided not to walk that day. I could no longer visualise any future benefits of not walking or the detrimental impact this walk would have on my progress to overcome the eating disorder. All I could focus on was putting my shoes on and leaving the house to walk in my habitual and addictive way, immediately feeling a sense of calm from that dopamine hit as I did so. The *now appeal* certainly held me in the eating disorder's addictive behaviours for many years. It's real and powerful.

## How Do You Address the Now Appeal?

First and foremost, like so much when it comes to overcoming an eating disorder, it takes recognising what's happening on a brain-based level. Use this to inform yourself why you feel the way you do, why you have the strongly compulsive urges and what makes the future hard to visualise when your compulsions strike. Information can be powerful to enable you to develop more self-compassion and find ways forward.

Overcoming the *now appeal* also begins with developing your own sense of self-trust. Believe in your ability to have a future that is bigger than the life you have pursuing these addictive eating disordered behaviours, no matter how attractive they feel in the moment.

Identify your future goals. These need to be meaningful and emotive to you and things that you want to experience in your future. Hold onto these goals and to who you are beyond the eating disordered behaviours. Envision your future and begin to strive towards it.

It can also help to remember that your life is on a continuum, and this is only a part of the journey. You had a past before this in which you did not have an eating disorder, and you can have a strong future in which the eating disorder is in your past.

As you envision your future self, pulling yourself out of the now, it can also be powerful to have a dialogue between you in the future and you now. Allow the person you are in the future to take your present self by the hand and reassure you that things are going to be better soon, if you stick it out and trust the process.

• • • ●•● • • •

# Confirmation Bias

Your brain is naturally hardwired to protect you. One of the ways this manifests is confirmation bias—something that affects us all. Confirmation bias is when your brain constantly scans the environment for anything that will reinforce your opinions or beliefs, because you have taught it that these beliefs are highly important to you. They can drive your actions, and therefore anything that confirms them matters. Unfortunately, your brain persists with this even if those beliefs are not actually correct.

Confirmation bias can also take over when you come across evidence that contradicts your beliefs. You are more likely to reject the incompatible evidence than you are to re-evaluate what you consider to be true and modify your beliefs based on new evidence. You might even experience a sense of personal challenge or attack from it.

When you spend time with people or move in social circles with others who hold the same beliefs as you, it will also reinforce the biased thoughts and opinions you might hold.

The consequence of confirmation bias is that it stops you being able to look at a situation from more than one angle.

This hardwired biased system that your brain is vulnerable to is important to understand when overcoming an eating disorder. Your brain will be seeking reasons to keep using those addictive behaviours or to get another hit from your *drug* of energy deficit. It will notice everything in your day-to-day life that reinforces the need to continue to restrict or engage in compensatory behaviours. Some of these will be twisted to fit with the beliefs that have served the eating disorder so well for so long. Unless you are vigilant, this will all happen below your conscious awareness.

Anyone with a restrictive eating disorder is likely to have developed a belief system that supports the idea that it would be wrong to eat without some level of restriction, resting is harmful and gaining weight a fate worse than death. This belief system has programmed your brain to be blind to any evidence that contradicts these highly dangerous beliefs that drive the eating disorder. As a result, it's likely that you have stopped noticing—let alone paying attention to—the huge range of foods on offer, the clear evidence that your body is struggling and the people who could be a more meaningful part of your life if you let them. On the flip side, your brain will very quickly notice and bring to your attention any diet culture messages, something someone else says about food, weight or fitness and tight-fitting clothes.

To override the natural tendency of your brain towards confirmation bias, make a conscious effort to keep an open mind. Be aware that your brain is biased towards not noticing all the things in front of you every day that will help you to overcome the eating disorder. Allow yourself to seek out information that supports the idea of unrestricted eating and resting as positive, healthy behaviours, particularly when overcoming a state of semi-starvation. See all the amazing opportunities for food, eating, living and being that are in the world for you to enjoy, and look to them with a positive sense of curiosity. Consider who you spend time with. If you're always surrounded by people who are into dieting or very fitness and body focused, then this will only reinforce your brain's existing biases. Explore the idea of joining social groups who can broaden your view that *everyone eats restrictively or controls their weight*; I can tell you that they definitely don't.

Finally, remember that our beliefs and thoughts ultimately change through our actions and emotional experiences, so putting in the action to overcome the eating disorder and applying positive emotions where you can will, over time, lead to a change in your beliefs. When this happens, your brain will instead seek out information to support these new positive beliefs that make up your free future.

· · · ● ·● ● · · ·

# Social Isolation

Eating disorders, just like any addiction, thrive in isolation. That's not to say that being isolated or lonely causes eating disorders, but it's a strong factor in maintaining them. In this way, isolation can make overcoming an eating disorder significantly more challenging.

When a restrictive eating disorder develops, it gives you a high level of reward response when you engage in behaviours that lead to energy deficit. This initial sense of reward is more powerful than the rewards you experience from other things—things that throughout evolution have given people a strong sense of well-being. Connection to others is a key example, where pursuit of your *drug* can take on greater value to your brain than spending time with others.

As discussed earlier in the book, an eating disorder also becomes a very effective method to numb negative emotions and stress. Once the eating disorder is giving you these feelings of safety and sense of calm, other sources of pleasure or things that form your identity become much less interesting or worth pursuing. Over time, you can even begin to forget about these other things or how to find them. This leads to a decline in where you go, the activities you engage in and the life you experience.

Pursuing affection or even conversation can begin to feel pointless and hold much less interest to you as your brain is numb to the simple pleasures this connection usually provides. As a result, connections to others become more shallow, and your social world contracts. This narrowing of your external world can parallel the narrowing of some key neural networks in your brain.

With an eating disorder you might find that your friendships have suffered, relationships been lost and your ability to communicate honestly and regularly with loved ones has reduced or faded completely. This can leave you feeling much less socially included, and the networks in your brain constrict. Instead of having multiple pathways to explore different life purposes and rewards, your brain narrows in line with the environments and situations you put yourself in. This limited world can make it feel as if you are living in an isolated prison.

There is a key study that highlights the power of connection to others when it comes to addictive disorders, referred to as the *rat park study*[2], conducted in the '70s and '80s. In this study, rats who were isolated in a cage were offered two types of water, one that was laced with drugs like morphine and one that was plain. The isolated rats were observed to drink the water laced with drugs and disregard the plain water, and they would continue to do so until eventually it killed them. However, when the same experiment was done on rats who were put in a cage with other rats and allowed to socialise, play, cuddle and interact, the results were very different. The rats who were not isolated opted to drink the plain water, ignoring the option with the drugs. This study highlights the importance that social connection has on overriding our need to numb or stimulate by artificial means.

Another study[3] investigated the effects of hand holding on the activation of brain structures to cope with stressful situations. This study found that people exposed to electric shocks experience less stress when they can hold hands, even with a stranger, than if they are alone. There is also evidence to demonstrate that having other people in your immediate proximity in the same room—even if there is no physical contact or conversation—is important in reducing the sense of isolation and stress you experience. This positive impact is far more significant than any form of communication or contact through a device.

I'm a fan of the work of Johann Hari, who has written a lot about both addiction and depression. He is often quoted as saying that *the opposite of addiction is connection*. While I don't think connection is the only solution to an addiction or eating disorder, I do believe it's very hard, if not impossible, to overcome an addictive or eating disorder in isolation.

Therefore, connection is vital to overcome an eating disorder, even or perhaps especially when the thing you most want to do is isolate. Overcoming an eating disorder means rediscovering natural sources of things that give you that sense of safety, acceptance and pleasure outside the eating disorder behaviours. As our brains have changed very little since our ancestors' day, it's key to seek out natural sources of safety and pleasure in the same way they would have done. Connection to others is one of the most significant. After all, we are wired to live in tribes and thrive on companionship. Connection releases healthy levels of dopamine and other rewarding neurochemicals, such as oxytocin, which help to keep your brain in balance. Connection also reduces cortisol levels.

When you consider the evolutionary theory of eating disorders, which is discussed fully in Chapter 7, the reason our ancestors who had developed the typical eating disorder characteristics survived once they reached a new and rich foraging ground was because of the connection with their loved ones. The gentle support their family provided to encourage them to start eating again and emerge from energy deficit is the very thing that enabled them to override the compulsions to restrict and move. Social connection and support from people who care about you can make all the difference.

Therefore, even if it feels the most difficult thing to do, seek out more connection with real, in-person (not just online) friends or family. If you have isolated so much through the years of having an eating disorder that old relationships are lost, seek out ways to connect with new people and form a social network.

People who do go through the process of overcoming an eating disorder find that as they break those old habits and behaviours, their interest in social connection grows. It becomes easier to enjoy time with people in a light-hearted way, to laugh again and actually experience fun in small ways. You might not feel that you want to connect with others at first, but push yourself to do it anyway. It will get easier, and it will help you form new brain networks that enable you to have a broader life with much wider interests. This is also a key factor to protect against the risk of relapse.

Eating disorders thrive in isolation. Overcoming one in isolation will be much harder than it needs to be, especially when you are facing swings in emotions and the temptation to return to old numbing habits to feel safe again. Opening yourself back up to social connection is something that takes courage. It means making yourself vulnerable. But it's perhaps one of the most important things you can do to enhance and protect your journey to overcome the eating disorder.

• • • ● ● • ● ● • • •

# The Return of Emotions

Even though an eating disorder doesn't initially develop purely as a way to manage hard emotions or life stress, the addictive nature of it and the surge of positive feelings that pursuing energy deficit brings very quickly changes this. The pursuit of energy deficit through restrictive eating and compulsive compensatory behaviours enables you to feel calm and generally good. This effect ensures that rapidly after onset, the eating disorder becomes the most powerful way you will ever have to numb painful emotions, feel better and manage stress.

As with any addiction, an eating disorder takes over and consumes the person at the centre of it. This means that your ability to experience a wider life shrinks away, and your ability to feel either good or bad emotions beyond a basic level disappears. This is due to a brain whose primary focus is the pursuit of energy deficit and its numbing effects. A change in emotional state and lack of ability to find joy in things that were once pleasurable is also a normal reaction to an energy-deprived brain, which anyone in a state of energy deficit will also be affected by (see Chapter 9 for information on starvation syndrome).

As you continue to live with an eating disorder, you can lose the ability to associate with your true emotions. This means you lose connection to yourself and to your ability to live authentically. When you are unable to recognise what you feel, it's hard to understand what your needs are beyond the inner compulsion to pursue energy deficit and to build a life around that addictive drive.

Many people have lived within the eating disordered and addicted brain for years, sometimes decades, so it's been years or decades since they experienced real emotions. This is something that's also hard for people to accept. When being numb has been your norm for years, it's hard to remember or understand that you are not experiencing emotions in the way other people do because what's *normal* is quickly forgotten. This makes it even more alarming when emotions do begin to resurface.

As you abstain from the compulsive behaviours in the process of overcoming the eating disorder, emotions begin to re-emerge, and they can be intense. This is a frightening and overwhelming time, and it can create an obstacle in continuing to push forwards as these powerful emotions automatically create stronger urges to return to the eating disordered behaviours.

Of course, it's not just negative emotions that resurface. Positive ones do too, which can be incredible as you feel real joy or genuine laughter again. You are likely to have positive feelings of relief that you are no longer living a life of entrapment in an eating disorder and perceive colour returning to your world in all kinds of small ways. However, even the return of positive emotions can feel like a double-edged sword as it can be tinged with intense sadness that you lost this ability to experience real pleasure for so long. Alongside this, experiencing joy again can be coupled with vulnerability and fears: *What if all these good changes are snatched away again?*

The ability to feel even more intense love and affection for friends and family also becomes stronger as your emotions reawaken. Of course, the love was always there, but with the eating disorder, it's often not felt so intensely. The return of this strength of emotional feeling towards others can also be frightening, although powerful.

When emotions strengthen towards others in your life, so, too, can feelings of pain and guilt around the impact that the eating disorder had, not just on your life but the lives of those who love you too. When you were consumed within the eating disorder, it was very difficult to notice or do anything about the impact that the eating disorder had on those around you. The harsh reality often only hits as you overcome the eating disorder and the narrowed focus that it created begins to widen again. These can be challenging emotions to sit with.

Many people experience feelings of guilt and shame in relation to the impact the eating disorder has had on those they love, as well as on themselves. There can also be wider feelings of shame related to the eating disorder. Shame is an incredibly painful emotion and hard to tolerate. Experiencing it can lead to powerful urges to re-engage in old behaviours for their numbing effects.

Boredom, feeling low and flat are also very common in the process of abstaining from the eating disorder. Your go-to for a sense of pleasure has been the eating disorder behaviours for a long time, and other pursuits people find pleasurable lost any appeal to you. When you make yourself stop the old habitual pleasure-seeking methods, you will feel lost and flat because your brain isn't yet capable of being able to enjoy pleasure in what might be considered *simpler* ways. This will occur as you are going through the dopamine deficit state and your natural dopamine levels are taking time to return to a natural and more stable baseline. To manage this, learning to tolerate boredom is going to be important, without using the eating disorder to numb it. It's also important to let yourself feel the hunger signals your brain and body are sending in times of boredom; this is when they can be most striking, and although its strength can be frightening, the hunger is there for a reason.

Finally, it's not uncommon for people to become very depressed at various stages of the process to overcome an eating disorder. In large part, this can be due to the dopamine deficit state that the addictive nature of the eating disorder created. Time is needed to allow dopamine levels to naturally return to a level balance. Of course, there are also other reasons people can go through episodes of depression in the process which are explored further below.

### What Purpose Do Emotions Serve?

Without getting into deep science of feelings and emotions, it's important to acknowledge that emotions and feelings serve a purpose. Humans don't have the capacity for emotions without good reason. As many people who have lived in the numb world of an eating disorder can testify to, it's very hard to live a truly full and meaningful life without the experience of emotions, both good and bad. But what are emotions and what purpose do they serve?

Most people don't realise that emotions occur before you are consciously aware of them. Emotions are essentially a physical state change that your brain then interprets—using its best guess as to what caused this change—and turns it into a *feeling*. This is the point at which your brain's interpretation of the change in physical state enters your conscious awareness. In this way, emotions can take over our thoughts and trigger immediate responses. This is often necessary for survival.

Emotions can serve the purpose of ensuring we are able to make quick decisions and deter from danger. For example, if you see a car heading towards you at high speed, fear is an appropriate emotion and serves the purpose of making you rapidly move out of the way.

Other purposes of emotions can include:

- A prompt to communicate with others. Emotions can guide you to seek connection and support;

- An aid to help you understand others;

- A deterrent from danger, aiding your survival;

- A guide to show you what is safe and good for you;

- A means to instruct you; and

- A means of allowing you to function on a social level and live among others, which is also important for survival.

When you can feel your emotions and recognise them, it can help you to identify what you need. For example:

- If you are feeling lonely, you might seek out someone for a hug or find ways to connect with others.

- If you are feeling overwhelmed, you might seek out quiet time to be by yourself.

- If you are frustrated and angry that your boss is constantly belittling you, you might seek a new job.

- If you feel guilt for forgetting your friend's birthday, you might call them to apologise and arrange a date to get together instead.

- If you are feeling sadness, you might recognise what has caused this and acknowledge that something important to you is missing, allowing yourself time to cry.

- When you feel joyful that you have conquered that large pizza AND the ice cream that the eating disorder stopped you from enjoying for so long, you might do a victory dance and share your win with someone who gets it!

Emotions are important. They are a valuable part of being human, and without them, life becomes suboptimal. But of course, emotions are not easy to experience. Many people use all kinds of measures to avoid feeling emotions. Eating disorders are one powerful method, but people without eating disorders might use alcohol, gambling, shopping, excessive social media use or other numbing habits.

When your emotions return as you overcome the eating disorder—which they will, and they need to—it will be crucial to find ways to manage them. The urge will be strong to resort to the old, effective eating disordered habits to block those emotions as they surface. Be prepared for this. Seek support, use a coach, use people who love you and develop a range of healthy skills in emotion regulation. Feel the painful emotions and let them guide you by recognising what they are trying to tell you. Then, allow yourself to wallow in the positive emotions, because after living in an eating disorder, you deserve to experience all the joy that life can now bring.

• • • ● • ● • • •

# Fear

Fear is a real and powerful factor that will affect your ability to overcome the eating disordered urges and compulsions. It can also impact on your motivation and self-belief about starting the process to overcome the eating disorder.

Before going further, the fear discussed in this section relates to the physiological fear reactions people can experience as they overcome an addictive disorder or eating disorder. This is not related specifically to fear of weight gain, which is discussed in much more detail in Chapter II.

Fear is something that controls our behaviours, often more than any of us realise or want to admit. When your brain and body are responding to fear, actions are taken unconsciously and automatically to ensure that you reach a place of safety as quickly as possible. That is, at least somewhere your brain perceives to be a place of safety.

The amygdala system was introduced earlier in relation to the part it plays in creating high levels of anxiety, stress and other withdrawal symptoms to drive an addiction. These withdrawal symptoms are the brain's attempt to motivate you towards pursuit of your *drug*. An activated brain stress system, creating strong fear reactions is a powerful motivation to resort back to the *drug's* numbing and rewarding effects.

When you have an eating disorder, your unconscious mind is doing all it can to get you closer to the energy deficit fix it craves so that it can avoid any levels of fear response and other difficult withdrawal symptoms. This results in your brain registering and wiring in the cause of these fear reactions to ensure it gets the rewards it seeks with greater ease in future. In this way, fear fuels the addictive nature of the eating disorder.

A fear reaction manifests on both a physical and emotional level.

Physically, your body enters what's commonly referred to as the fight-or-flight response—when your brain has perceived a danger, and your body prepares to fight the threat or to run from it. Physical changes occur, which include a rise in your heart rate, sweating, feeling agitated, faster breathing and increased alertness.

The emotional reaction relates to how your brain then translates the physical changes into your experience of it. This is created by the reasons you attribute to the physical state change. Therefore, these physical changes can feel terrifying, but they can also feel thrilling or exciting, as the physiological symptoms for these feelings are the same.

Of course, when you are experiencing a powerful fear reaction, you feel out of control and need to find a way to alleviate it fast. With the eating disorder, this can result in the drive to move away from whatever created the fear response. Many of you will relate to the fact that this fear reaction can be powerful when you are faced with unfamiliar food situations. These situations are a threat to your brain because they are the equivalent of not getting the safe and habitually rewarding fix from restriction and energy deficit. Escaping such a situation feels immediately soothing. This pattern of behaviour has the effect of reinforcing to your brain that escaping the situation was the correct action and that avoidance is the best strategy to use in future. Over time this makes food-related situations even more threatening, creating an increasing drive to avoid them.

Later in the book, the evolutionary, adapted flee-from-famine theory to restrictive eating disorders is explained in more detail. Touching on this now, though, your brain has developed evolutionary to deliberately push you towards the pursuit of energy deficit by engaging your amygdala and stress response systems. This is an effective method your brain can use to pursue the goal of food avoidance and constant movement to migrate. At one time this was crucial for survival of the tribe. Of course today, this fear response can keep you trapped in the eating disorder, even when it's damaging your life.

Up until now, the information discussed has related to the immediate fear reactions you will experience as you pursue abstinence behaviours to overcome an eating disorder. However, there are also other ways in which anxiety and fear can present when you are either in or contemplating entering the *recovery* process. These fears can include:

- Not coping with life without the eating disorder;

- Fear of failure at attempting to overcome the eating

disorder;

- Fear of change because the eating disorder is familiar and feels safe;

- Experiencing emotions and feelings again;

- A loss of identity;

- No longer having the numbing effects of the eating disorder and finding that life is not enjoyable without it; and

- Fear of success.

Perhaps the biggest fear many of you will relate to is the fear of change. The eating disorder is familiar and ultimately it might make you miserable, but familiar is comfortable and can feel safe. In this way, these future-focused, fear-based thoughts can keep you stuck with an eating disorder.

## How to Address Fear?

Firstly, understand the fear that you are experiencing. It's real and it's coming from old and powerful brain systems that have had years of evolution to perfect themselves. Recognise that the fear is your brain attempting to protect you in misguided ways.

To begin to overcome the fear and anxiety that's keeping you trapped in the eating disorder, take time to reflect on how it manifests for you. What drives it and how is it controlling you?

From this you can take steps to learn how to prevent the fear from overpowering you.

Below are some suggestions for ways to manage the fear as you are overcoming the eating disorder:

- Acknowledge any of your fears or anxieties and work through them, using others to support you in this process. What do the fears relate to?

- Recognise the powerful stories that your brain is coming up with as its way to drive you away from the things that generate the fear response. These stories are often seemingly rational and believable, but they are just thoughts. Very often they are also habits of thinking which are there because your brain has learnt that they are a very effective method to divert you from the things it perceives to be a threat. Identify these stories and habitual thoughts, finding new ways to respond to them.

- Take ownership for your decisions. When fear comes up, attempting to pull you back to the eating disorder behaviours, recognise what's happening and that you do have a choice in how to respond.

- Remember that you can feel fear but do it anyway. Approach the things that scare you. Use fear and resistance to doing things as your in-built sat-nav system, directing you to the path that you almost certainly need to take.

- Fear and anxiety are future-based reactions—worrying about what might be, not what is. Stay in the present moment and face what you must do here and now, allowing the future to sort itself out, because the anxiety is very often not grounded. Meditation can be powerful to develop skills in how to ground yourself.

- Consider the alternative to responding to the fear. Where has following the fear landed you? In contrast, what impact might facing the fear and moving forward actually have on your life?

- Expose yourself to the fear repeatedly so it becomes familiar. In this way, the fear reactions quickly become less intense and soon disappear altogether.

- Adopt a positive mindset. Find that *Can do!* attitude, work on your self-belief and let any shame go.

Fear can be powerful as you overcome a restrictive eating disorder. Understanding the fear and why it's there, along with developing tools to override it, will make all the difference.

• • • ● • ● • • •

# Work, Studies & the Constant Drive to Be Busy

I've met very few people with restrictive eating disorders who don't have an incessant energy and drive to be constantly doing. This can be working, studying, keeping busy with housework, looking after the children or helping local charities. Very often they are doing all these things in a single day. People with eating disorders are regularly applauded by those around them for their excellent work ethic, making the best employees and most dedicated students, and often have the cleanest of homes.

However, this drive to be busy is a strong symptom of a restrictive eating disorder. Chapter 7 covers the evolutionary theory to eating disorders, but the constant need to be on the go, which can be mentally and/or physically, largely relates to the migratory response that's triggered by energy deficit. This served our ancestors, who needed an unceasing drive to keep moving and searching for a new foraging ground and who could't afford to rest until food sources were located. It doesn't serve people today, and unless addressed it will impact on your ability to overcome the eating disorder.

The ongoing drive to be constantly busy is powerful when you experience it. The things you need to stay busy doing can feel of the upmost importance. Not doing them will feel impossible and unthinkable.

There are a few other key reasons why this drive to stay busy and the high priority you place on doing so have become so powerful and alluring:

- The impulse to be constantly alert, on the go and productive forms part of the addictive nature of the eating disorder. Staying productive gives you the same brain-based rewards (from dopamine) as those provided by restrictive eating and compensatory behaviours. To not be busy creates withdrawal symptoms and cravings in the same way abstaining from any of the other addictive behaviours do. Your brain also creates strong feelings of wrong-doing or shame if you're not engaged in some form of productive activity. This is another method it uses to push you into behaviours that will result in a fresh dopamine fix.

- Martyr complex is a key feature of an eating disorder, and this can also create an intense need to be productive and hence to be recognised by others as a good person. Martyr complex is explained alongside the evolutionary theory to eating disorders in the coming chapters.

- Although, for some, the urge to be busy can be met by mental productivity while sedentary, for most there is a related physical drive to be *on the go*. This coincides with compulsive movement and exercise, which is a strong feature of a restrictive eating disorder for most.

- Staying busy distracts from and blocks hunger. It's a learned behaviour that people with restrictive eating disorders who live in constant energy deficit use to blunt the uncomfortable and otherwise distressing hunger symptoms. Being busy makes it easier to continue to eat restrictively and feeds self-denial in relation to how hungry and malnourished you really are.

- Constantly being on the go enables you to deny how unhappy you are and how narrow your life has otherwise become because of the eating disorder. When you can get through each day in a haze of productivity, even if it culminates in ground hog misery in the longer term, it makes the present moment easier to tolerate. It keeps you feeling numb and able to function.

Staying busy, working long hours, studying and pursuing all the other day-to-day activities that keep you on the go will make the eating disorder harder to overcome. It's also very often a key factor in maintaining an eating disorder.

To address and overcome restrictive eating disorders, it's essential to apply mental energy and focus, time and rest. While you are still trying to do everything else, you won't have the necessary conscious focus you need to not only stop yourself from engaging in your usual eating disordered habits but to also develop new, *healthy* ones. For this your brain needs to reprogram. It requires as much of your focus as you can give to unlearn the old behaviours and habits, unwire the eating disordered brain networks and wire in completely new and separate circuits that will allow you to build a free future. Your dopamine levels need time to reset, which means sitting through very difficult withdrawal symptoms and cravings and being able to stop yourself from resorting automatically to old numbing behaviours as soon as something becomes too uncomfortable.

Reprogramming your brain is mentally exhausting and draining. You will feel strong urges to sleep at times, and being able to give in to this is important. Your brain needs a lot of sleep or deep rest for the full rewiring to take effect.

In addition to this, you need to get your body out of energy deficit. When you are experiencing extreme hunger and need to eat as much food as your body is asking you for, eating alone can be a full-time job!

The people I see who try to go through the process of overcoming an eating disorder while working or studying or not seeking support with household chores find it much harder to make meaningful progress. Returning to work or studies too soon into the process also inevitably comes with significant risk of undoing any progress made or progress stalling.

Staying busy and distracted does not give your brain the space and time it needs to reprogram. To you, being busy is another form of drug. It's a drug you also need to abstain from as far as possible. This means taking a step back from everything in your life you possibly can. Be honest about how much you can let go of for a while; it's more than you will want to admit. Wherever possible, stop work or at least reduce your hours. Take six months or a year away from your studies. Get help with household chores or childcare. Then use the time and space you have created to do the mental work needed. Allow yourself to address the eating disorder from every angle. Creating the space to do this will enable you to explore who you are without an eating disorder, building your self-identity without other influences that are potentially still shadowed by the eating disorder identity.

Taking time out will feel like a big step, but it can be an impactful one. Giving yourself a few months or even a year away from your ongoing life demands now will be worth it when it enables you to move forward and build a life that's not driven by an eating disorder—a life that carries more meaning, purpose and happiness than an eating disorder ever can.

---

1. Mandelli L, Draghetti S, Albert U, De Ronchi D, Atti AR. Rates of comorbid obsessive-compulsive disorder in eating disorders: A meta-analysis of the literature. J Affect Disord. 2020 Dec 1; 277:927-939. doi: 10.1016/j.jad.2020.09.003. Epub 2020 Sep 8. PMID: 33065835.

2. Alexander BK, Beyerstein BL, Hadaway PF, Coambs RB. Effect of early and later colony housing on oral ingestion of morphine in rats. Pharmacol Biochem Behav. 1981 Oct; 15(4):571-6. doi: 10.1016/0091-3057(81)90211-2. PMID: 7291261.

3. Coan JA, Sbarra DA. Social baseline theory: The social regulation of risk and effort. Curr Opin Psychol. 2015 Feb; 1:87-91. doi: 10.1016/j.copsyc.2014.12.021. PMID: 25825706; PMCID: PMC4375548.

# Chapter Six

---

# Self-Empowerment & Choice

## Self-Empowerment Is Critical

Self-empowerment is one of the most important factors in your ability to overcome an eating disorder successfully. This means taking control of your own process to overcome it and becoming confident in your abilities as you do so.

I often say to clients as they attempt to overcome an eating disorder's addictive pull that they need to *own their recovery*. When I say this, I'm talking about self-empowerment.

Self-empowerment relates to developing a mindset in which you believe in your own abilities and can take charge. You need to believe you can override the eating disorder's urges, stop the behaviours and eat more. You need to trust you can cope with changes to your body shape and weight. Finding the steps to take that will work for you and making them happen is key, as is seeking the type of support that you believe will make it easier for you to make the necessary changes. It's also crucial that as you go through the hugely difficult process of overcoming the eating disorder, you begin to develop a sense of identity beyond it.

Self-empowerment is not being told what to do and only doing it because someone else says you should. It's not seeking permission to eat or rest or gain weight. It's not blaming others when things don't go as you hoped. It's recognising that this process is hard and emotionally challenging, and so lapses can be inevitable. It's learning from the lapses when they occur, taking responsibility without being self-critical and then taking the next step forward.

Self-empowerment is the very thing that allows you to take control of the eating disorder and problem-solve all the necessary but challenging steps to overcome it. When you become self-empowered, you take your control back from the eating disorder. It's liberating and it can give you a sense of achievement, self-pride, confidence and self-worth.

### Why Do So Many People with Eating Disorders Lack Skills in Self-Empowerment?

Many people with eating disorders lack the the necessary factors needed to be self-empowered. This is often due to having had an eating disorder for years, previously unsuccessful *recovery* attempts and, for some, prescriptive treatment that has removed their self-trust and independence. Some people have even been told that their ability to ever overcome the eating disorder is minimal at best.

For years, I too lacked any sense of self-empowerment to overcome the eating disorder. And despite an inner desperation to overcome it, after a few short years of having an eating disorder, I was given the prognosis that my poor quality of life was the best I could ever hope for. This left me defeated, submissive and distrusting of myself. I'd seek the permission of others rather than make decisions for myself about how I could make the necessary changes to find the free future I craved.

It was only after years of living in this way that I accepted that the treatment approach I had tried over and again was never going to work. I knew I had to find another way forward. This led me to finally take charge of the process to overcome the eating disorder. I decided that I was going to overcome it, and I was going to do it my way. This was when things finally started to change.

Traditional treatment could make me gain weight, but nothing ever changed at a brain-based level, and so the eating disorder and all the addictive behaviours never left me. Change only happened when I decided that I was going to break the restrictive eating, stop the behaviours and put myself through the emotional processes on a path that was my own. I was determined to do it no matter how tough it got, how much weight I gained or how quickly. I had to stop seeking permission to make changes or looking for excessive reassurance. A professional, family member or coach telling me exactly what to eat and when would never work. They could support me when things got tough and help me process my thoughts, emotions and next steps, but I had to make the changes, take the steps and do it. It was my life, and I knew I couldn't live with the eating disorder for the rest of my days. I had to find out if my life could be different, and to do that, I had to take back my control. When I did this, things shifted mentally in ways they never had before. I felt more liberated than I had in years and finally believed that perhaps I could have a future without the eating disorder being a part of it.

## Self-Empowerment Involves Self-Trust, Belief, Identity and a Future Vision

To feel self-empowered means to have trust in yourself. This is something so many people with eating disorders, perhaps understandably, lack.

You lose trust in your own ability to say no to the eating disorder behaviours. If time and again you have been determined that *tomorrow I will eat more*, but when tomorrow comes you eat all the same restrictive foods you always do, self-trust in your abilities is quickly lost. One of the reasons for this difficulty to keep saying no to the eating disordered urges is ego fatigue, which was discussed in the previous chapter. This is where your brain runs out of energy when it comes to constantly stopping strong impulses. Ego fatigue is also impacted by self-trust. People who have lost belief in themselves are known to be more affected by ego fatigue than people who believe they can control their behaviours.

The other factor that impacts your trust in yourself is dopamine, which relates to the urgent and powerful drive to get that energy deficit *fix*. Pursuing energy deficit creates an instantly calming, soothing effect, and the dopamine release pushes you to pursue this and delay the pain for another day. This relates to the concept of delay discounting or the *now appeal*, which only adds to how hard the eating disorder urges are to resist (the *now appeal* was also discussed in Chapter 5).

Your self-identity will also impact your sense of empowerment in relation to overcoming the eating disorder. To find the strength and willpower to go through the processes necessary to overcome an eating disorder and resist the frequent and strong urges, you need to believe in a future self who is not someone with an eating disorder. And you need to trust that it will be worth the pain to get there. When you have lived life in a numb eating disorder bubble for any length of time, your identity becomes entwined in it. It's then hard to envision let alone trust in a future without the eating disorder forming part of your identity.

Ultimately, you need to find ways to develop your self-trust and belief in yourself and your abilities to make changes. You also need to create and hold on to a vision of a future that has't had the colour drained from it by an eating disorder. As you develop these skills, you feel more empowered and are then able to take further steps towards overcoming the eating disorder, which positively impacts your self-identity, confidence and feelings of self-worth.

When you begin to develop trust in yourself, you will become more empowered. This can then drive you to take further steps toward behaviour change, and as you do, you come to trust yourself a little more, and the process continues to evolve. But, of course, to take those first steps, you need to have some initial belief in yourself. Tell yourself that just because previous attempts haven't worked, it doesn't mean you can't do it now. You are not the same person you were when you attempted to overcome the eating disorder before. You are more knowledgeable; you have more insight and perhaps more determination. Think of other hard things you have done in your life and remind yourself that you are a strong person, and you can empower yourself to overcome this eating disorder, even when the process gets hard.

### Traditional Treatment Models for Eating Disorders Can Disempower People

*Before getting into this section, I want to emphasise that this is not meant to discourage anyone from entering traditional treatment if that's what you need and decide to do. This section is to raise awareness of where some of the risks lie in traditional, medical models of treatment so you can benefit from the support they can offer while holding onto your own sense of self, drive and purpose.*

Traditional treatment models for eating disorders, which many treatment providers still either fully or partially adhere to, are based on medical models. These models treat eating disorders as a *disease* for which the *patient* must be treated by doctors or health professionals.

There are a few problems with this.

Firstly, a lot of doctors in most of the world don't have the training, time, experience or actual insight needed to effectively manage people with eating disorders. This is a sad reality of our times, and the extreme pressures on health services mean other conditions take priority.

Secondly, doctors and psychiatrists are educated to treat patients by medicine. This means prescribing drugs or other forms of non-invasive or invasive procedures and, if these fail to work, mitigating the blame. Sadly, it's not uncommon when it comes to eating disorders for this blame to be put onto the *patient,* who is labelled *treatment resistant* or *non-compliant.*

Thirdly, when a person with an eating disorder is given the label of being the *patient,* they can assume a submissive role. The medical model can prevent people from attempting to develop their own tools in self-management or self-control; instead they seek external resources to fix or problem-solve for them. Over time, this leaves them feeling increasingly hopeless or helpless, losing any trust in themselves that they might have once had.

An example of this is that when you enter traditional treatment, you are often given a prescribed plan of what to eat and when. You are told to disengage from other behaviours either immediately or by reducing them in a structured way. You don't have to think for yourself as you find yourself in this paternalistic, *do as I say* approach. And truthfully, when you have had an eating disorder for several years and you are worn down by feeling that you can't trust yourself, then being told what to do can be a relief, at least at first. However, it also removes your independence, trust in your own abilities and sense of responsibility for your own journey.

An eating disorder develops over time into a powerful way to calm your emotions, reduce anxiety and help you feel normal enough to function. It's effectively the best coping strategy you will ever have. Therefore, to overcome it, as you disengage from the restriction and other behaviours, you need to find other coping strategies to replace them which you need motivation to develop and use. This comes from self-empowerment. It can't work if you rely on someone else to fix you.

To overcome an eating disorder, an internal locus of control is needed. You need to believe that you, not external forces, have control over the outcome of things happening in your life. The medical model of treating eating disorders often undermines this, as it fosters a dependence on prescriptive treatment.

Support, advice, information and encouragement are all vital when overcoming an eating disorder, but ultimately without the person at the centre of the disorder being self-empowered, the rest will never be sufficient. You need to know that you have control over your own process.

You need to believe in a future that is not devoid of real-life opportunities, of fun, laughter and colour because of an ever-present eating disorder. Most importantly, too, no matter how long you have had an eating disorder, you must be allowed to believe that you have a future beyond it.

## People Do Recover Without Treatment

It's not an exaggeration to say that overcoming an eating disorder is likely the most difficult thing you will ever do. I often liken it to someone overcoming a heroin addiction, with the same intense level of withdrawal symptoms, cravings and emotional turmoil. It's a process that's emotionally demanding; it requires significant changes to daily behaviours and habits, as well as the need to tolerate physical symptoms and body changes.

The process to overcome an eating disorder isn't smooth for anyone, and it does necessitate a high degree of support. You should never expect yourself or be expected by others to overcome an eating disorder in isolation. Community is important, even if that team or community supporting you through the process is made up of only two or three people. It matters. The less important factor is the professional status of those people. Yes, if you are medically compromised you absolutely need to be monitored and supported to ensure you are physically safe enough to keep pushing forward in the eating and recovery process. If you feel very emotionally unstable and at risk of harming yourself or others, then you need intense support from the appropriate medical teams. Beyond these concerns, health professionals might make up part of your primary support team, but they are not a necessity. The team you recruit in this process needs to be made up of people you trust, people who hold belief for you, who can motivate, encourage and perhaps guide but not lead.

Some people reading this now will be doing so in absolute shock that I dare suggest that medical treatment need not be pursued when overcoming something as powerful as an eating disorder. I understand that, but if medical treatment worked, then why do so many people revolve in and out of those doors so many times over?

Research also backs up the idea that medical treatment isn't always necessary to overcome an eating disorder. There are studies available that indicate between 50–66 percent of people with eating disorders recover *spontaneously* over time[123]. In plain English, this means they overcome the eating disorder without ever receiving medical treatment. This doesn't mean they didn't have any support from other sources but that they didn't touch medical services for support.

Despite these figures and as the authors of one study into the idea of *spontaneous recovery* for eating disorders identify[4], professionals remain sceptical and underestimate the impor-tance of self-change in their patients with eating disorders.

This attitude only prevents these professionals from learning from the people they are there to treat and maintains outdated practices.

### The Term *Treatment Resistant*

Labelling a person with an eating disorder as *treatment resistant* is another thing that removes all self-confidence, self-trust and self-belief from them.

Some reading this will be all too familiar with the term *treatment resistant*. It is a term that even today is used frequently in traditional eating disorder treatment services.

This is when a person who has an eating disorder and has been in treatment for a given length of time is blamed for the fact that they aren't improving. By this point, the person being described has usually had any remaining self-worth, esteem and belief in themselves sucked dry, leaving them completely disempowered.

The term *treatment resistant* should be banned from being used about anyone, let alone someone with an eating disorder. It stops people believing in their own abilities; it tells them they might never get better and leaves them feeling completely hopeless and helpless.

For any of you who have been labelled *treatment resistant* in the past, perhaps now is the time to reframe this label so kindly bestowed on you.

It's not inconceivable that someone with an eating disorder absolutely NEEDS to be treatment resistant to the traditional model of treatment to get well. If the current medical model of treatment ultimately disempowers people, then by resisting that, perhaps a sense of empowerment can be reclaimed. Start to resist being told that your best chance at any sort of quality of life is by doing as you are told, and instead claim your own agency. When you do this, you begin to develop belief in yourself and prove to others what you are truly capable of. As your self-belief grows, you will begin to consider the idea of having a future beyond the eating disorder and beyond life as a *patient*. Continue to grow in these ways, and you will begin to understand what you need to do to take those first important steps forward to stop the behaviours, change those habits and do what's necessary for you to overcome the eating disorder.

### Self-Empowerment Does Not Mean Going Through the Process Alone

Throughout this chapter on self-empowerment and how important it is in the process of overcoming an eating disorder, I've tried to be clear that taking ownership of the process doesn't mean you go through it without support or any form of treatment. Overcoming an eating disorder in isolation isn't the idea.

To be self-empowered is the opposite of going through the process alone.

If you think about anyone who accomplishes anything big in life (and overcoming an eating disorder is up there with the biggest thing anyone will do in a lifetime), they have a team behind them. Sometimes they have global-scale teams behind them! These teams are there to help, support, guide, encourage, problem-solve and improve their overall chances of success while they remain at the centre of the process, taking responsibility for it. Own your process in overcoming the eating disorder and use all the help you can get. Take the driver's seat but use your team to keep you on track in the journey, to encourage and guide you, to help you overcome obstacles and to celebrate wins with you. Allow your team to make the process easier in any way they can while you maintain control of the wheel.

## Self-Empowerment Is Key for Reprogramming Your Brain

Reprogramming your brain is fundamental when it comes to overcoming an eating disorder and the addictive behaviours that go with it. As already discussed, this involves unwiring the old brain circuits that drive the addictive habits and wiring in new circuits that will drive healthier habits to replace them. For this you are using your brain's neuroplasticity, which is much more effective when you are an active participant in the process. This means you need to be making the decision to change, problem-solving how and instigating those changes.

When learning anything new, your brain needs to understand that the new learning is important and so it helps to apply emotions. You need to dig into your inner motivation, looking to what not having an eating disorder can bring you and summoning up feelings of excitement and anticipation. This motivation will also help drive you to keep going when the process gets tough. Believe in your abilities and celebrate steps forward. Celebrating the small wins promotes the increased release of dopamine in response to behaviours you want, which can help motivate you to repeat them.

The second component of reprogramming your brain in overcoming an eating disorder is that of the dopamine reset. This is when you will experience some potentially distressing and uncomfortable withdrawal effects as you stop engaging in the eating disorder behaviours and experience the dopamine deficit created through the years of engaging in them.

Self-empowerment will help you find ways to tolerate these withdrawal symptoms rather than allowing them to trigger you back into the addictive and numbing behaviours. Understanding why you feel this way and taking control to recognise the discomfort and yet deciding to sit with it is empowering. You will also need to problem-solve so that you can identify what support systems will help you when the emotional or physical withdrawal symptoms are intense. You know yourself best when it comes to what support makes a difference and who that should come from. You, more than anyone, know the key triggers that are likely to push you back into the addictive and habitual behaviours. Other people can help you identify these triggers, but no one can tell you what yours are without your input. Choosing to be honest in the process is another thing that only you can do. This means being honest with yourself and with your support team. At the end of the day, all these factors relate back to being sufficiently empowered and motivated.

For brain reprogramming to be as effective as it can be in overcoming an eating disorder, it's vital to take control of the process, choose to change, build on new behaviours each day while stopping the old ones and put in place support that will make a difference to you. Believe that you can keep going—even when withdrawal symptoms are strong—and develop a self-identity for your future without the eating disorder. Developing your own sense of self-empowerment and taking ownership of your process are critical.

**To Conclude**

People who have overcome eating disorders say that two things were key to the process: empowerment to do so and self-reconciliation, which means to learn more about themselves and their self-identity[5].

It is possible for you to be supported in developing skills in self-empowerment, alongside skills in emotional regulation and self-control. Support and encouragement are also critical when the process of overcoming the eating disorder feels exhausting and distressing.

Meaningful change doesn't happen through a prescription or treatment to a passive *patient*. You need to be active in your process because your future life is at stake.

In my experience, when people are shown what they can and need to do for themselves and then are supported through it, they very often can and will make changes, developing pride in themselves when they do. This gives them a stronger sense of self-drive, purpose and, of course, self-empowerment.

· · · ● · ● · · ·

# Is an Eating Disorder a Choice?

The concept of choice is one that generates a lot of debate when it comes to eating disorders, as well as other addictions. Do you choose to develop an eating or addictive disorder? How much choice do you have in overcoming it?

When you have an eating disorder, these conversations can create negative emotional states such as shame, weakness or low self-worth. It's then inevitable that these difficult feelings will add to the challenge you face in making the necessary changes to overcome the eating disorder.

But if there is no element of choice in terms of at least overcoming an eating or addictive disorder, then how is it that people do overcome them and sometimes even without professional support?

Firstly, though, let's explore the question as to whether you choose to develop an eating disorder or an addiction.

The answer to this is a black–and–white NO.

You do not choose to develop eating disorders or other forms of addiction. For people with drug addictions, the only choice they made might have come when they took that very first experimental or recreational drug. For some, the drug they become addicted to was prescribed by a doctor. They wouldn't have foreseen that they would be pulled into ongoing drug use and the consequences this would have on their lives.

If you have a restrictive eating disorder, the only conscious choice you might have made was to start an innocent diet or an exercise kick. Perhaps the choice was inflicted on you by well-meaning parents or professionals, encouraging you to lose weight for *your health*. When you did so, you had no insight into the consequences. You couldn't have predicted the energy deficit that the *harmless* diet created would lead you into a dangerous and life-limiting eating disorder.

Therefore, no, you do not and did not choose to develop an eating disorder.

But what about overcoming the eating disorder? Is there a deliberate choice you make in terms of overcoming it or not?

When an eating disorder takes hold, it serves as a powerful way to soothe pain. Even when the initial attraction that was once present to the behaviours no longer holds any rational appeal, or the behaviours have very possibly become repellent, they still retain a powerful allure. This is because they blunt mental pain, suppress crippling withdrawal symptoms, allow you to avoid the fear reactions that arise from making changes, and they ease cravings.

Plus, at the end of the day, brains are biology. They have biases, attractions, associations to things and habitual thought patterns that can all drive automatic behaviours. Your brain is strongly driven by emotions, desires or fears and rarely by logic. And brains are changed at a deep level by an eating disorder when it comes to embedded brain circuits that will push you with force to pursue your *drug* of energy deficit.

To say that you are continuing to pursue eating disordered behaviours as a choice is not a reasonable statement. Today neuroscientists have learnt that in all of us, any decisions that we believe we are making at a conscious and rational level are in fact made by the unconscious part of our brain around half a second before they enter our conscious awareness[6]. This means we all have less deliberate agency over our actions than even the most self-controlled amongst us believe they do.

But people *do* overcome eating and addictive disorders, and when they do so, choice and self-control are key factors. The cravings to engage in the behaviours are outside your control, yet you do have a level of control over whether you act on those cravings.

Studies show that many people with other forms of addiction stop by the age of thirty without professional help, even after years of addictive behaviours[7]. This indicates that there is a degree of choice they have made to overcome the addiction. In these cases, overcoming the addiction correlates to factors such as the absence of other health conditions, marital status (where single people stay addicted longer, which ties into the importance of connection); economic pressures or concerns about losing the respect of children or other family members. It would therefore appear that clear and important incentives will help you to make the necessary changes. This also relates back to the topic of the *now appeal*. The seemingly best choice in the current moment can be the worst long-term choice, but it's hard to see it as such in the here and now. When faced with reasons to engage with the addiction or reasons not to, the option of easing the pain in the moment can feel most attractive.

We also know that severe addictions and eating disorders will narrow your focus and reduce your ability to get pleasure from experiences that are not related to pursuing the hit from your *drug*.

However, people will still react to incentives and things they want from their future, if they believe these things are possible for them. The ability to choose to stop and to find the strength to make this choice depends on your having very meaningful reasons to do so. Even then, it's more complicated to overcome a compulsive behaviour than just saying no to it. It takes hard work, mental effort, focus and support from others, but you can make choices towards the discovery of new opportunities if you are able to believe that you can and you are empowered to do so.

**You Can**

The ability to make changes and overcome compulsions is within you. But it will come from how you perceive your options and your choices, alongside your ability to recognise the impact of continuing to pursue the behaviours.

Urges created by an eating disorder can be incredibly strong, but so too can the human capacity for self-control, even if it's at a diminished level. Self-control can be used to pull yourself back from acting on an addictive desire, even when it's painful, anxiety provoking and holds risk of failure. Resisting the lure of the behaviours and the hit they create is not impossible, but it is incredibly difficult.

Support to make the necessary changes also needs to be available at the time you are seeking it. When you have found the drive to make changes and chosen to do so, it's vital that that moment is not lost by your having to wait six months for support. The time in which you are ready is a critical moment in which to harness your brain's drive for desire and focus it in a brand-new direction.

When it comes to overcoming an eating disorder, there is choice involved. But you do need to believe in your abilities to change. When you are told that the eating disorder is chronic, it puts the burden onto you and removes your understanding that you do have the choice to overcome it. It disempowers you when what you need above all else is to be empowered.

If this is your situation now, then you need to recognise that the eating disorder is not something you want anymore, notice that it's wrecking your life and destroying your future opportunities, and you want things to be different. You do have the choice to decide that you will stop the behaviours in the pursuit of energy deficit. If you make that choice, you are more likely to do it.

For this to work, you also need a focus on new goals, pursuits and a life outside the eating disorder. You need strong reasons that are emotive to you as to why you will change. Allow these goals to drive your desire for more, nurture them and choose to move towards them.

Work on your self-belief in your abilities and trust in yourself so you are better able to override even the most powerful and alluring of urges. Understand what your brain is doing when those cravings hit and the impact that the *now appeal* can have so you are better able to resist it.

You didn't choose to have an eating disorder or deliberately set out on that path, and choosing to overcome an eating disorder is far from simple or easy. It's not about simple choice. It is far more complicated, so don't feel you are to blame just because you have not succeeded yet in overcoming the eating disorder. You must remove any self-blame that might be there.

There are choices to be made to overcome the eating disorder, but it takes support, empowering yourself and finding meaningful goals beyond it so that you can keep making the choice to move towards your goals, even when the *now appeal* sets in.

---

1. Cotrufo, P, Monteleone, P, Castaldo, E, & Maj, M. (2004). A 4-year epidemiological study of typical and atypical eating disorders: Preliminary evidence for subgroups of atypical eating disorders with different natural outcomes. European Eating Disorders Review, 12(4), 234-239.

2. Faravelli C, Ravaldi C, Truglia E, Zucchi T, Cosci F, Ricca V. Clinical epidemiology of eating disorders: results from the Sesto Fiorentino study. Psychother Psychosom. 2006; 75(6):376-83. doi: 10.1159/000095444. PMID: 17053339.

3. Keski-Rahkonen A, Hoek HW, Susser ES, Linna MS, Sihvola E, Raevuori A, Bulik CM, Kaprio J, Rissanen A. Epidemiology and course of anorexia nervosa in the community. Am J Psychiatry. 2007 Aug; 164(8):1259-65. doi: 10.1176/appi.ajp.2007.06081388. PMID: 17671290.

4. Walter Vandereycken (2012). Self-Change in Eating Disorders: Is "Spontaneous Recovery" Possible? Eating Disorders, 20:2, 87-98, DOI: 10.1080/10640266.2012.6539424.

5. Duncan, TK, Sebar, B, & Lee, J. (2015). Reclamation of power and self: A meta-synthesis exploring the process of recovery from anorexia nervosa. Advances in Eating Disorders, 3(2), 177-190.

6. Budson AE, Richman KA, Kensinger EA. Consciousness as a memory system. Cogn Behav Neurol. 2022 Dec 1; 35(4):263-297. doi: 10.1097/WNN.0000000000000319. PMID: 36178498; PMCID: PMC9708083.

7. Heyman, GM (2013). Addiction and choice: theory and new data. Front. Psychiatry 4:31. doi: 10.3389/fpsyt.2013.00031.

# Chapter Seven

# The Evolutionary Theory for Restrictive Eating Disorders

## Evolution and Addictive Disorders

You could be forgiven for asking why the brain has evolved to be capable of developing destructive addictions.

Yet evolution can often explain why the symptoms or characteristics of conditions typically considered a mental illness in today's culture were once beneficial to our ancestors and even key for their basic survival. In today's modern world where everything is available at the touch of a button and we don't have the same primal threats to our safety, some of these evo-lutionary brain systems are unhelpful and even problematic. Addictive and eating disorders are a key example.

With an addiction, people initially engage in a *drug* that creates pleasurable effects and positive emotions. The positive emotions arise from the brain's evolved reward systems, which you now understand involve the release of natural opiates and dopamine.

In our ancestors' day, the purpose of the reward system was to ensure people found pleasure in essential things for survival like food, shelter, sex and safety, so they felt motivated to continue pursuing these rewards. The brain is then primed to learn from them. This involves the brain noticing and forming associations between the rewarding experiences and factors in the environ-ment as well as to internal states, such as emotions or physical sensations. These associations then become powerful future triggers to pursue the same rewarding experience again.

We know then why the brain has evolved to pursue goals, particularly those that take us to the good things in life. Un-fortunately, the brain wasn't prepared for the diverse range of highly rewarding substances and behaviours that are available in the modern world. Substances and behaviours that are so rewarding, our brains learn to pursue them above and beyond other things in life.

## Why Do Some People Develop Addictions and Not Others?

Some of you will now be asking this question. If our brains have this ability to pursue highly rewarding *drugs*, and these are now so freely available, why doesn't everyone develop an addiction?

Many people can drink when they fancy a beer or wine socially but don't become dependent. Some people can gamble without it becoming a problem, while others develop a powerful drive to continue to gamble to the point that it destroys their relationships and careers.

From an evolutionary perspective, different members of the tribe would need to find pleasure in and be motivated to pursue different goals to ensure the survival of the whole tribe. Therefore, one person's brain might be adapted to find more reward in hunting, while another would be more motivated to seek or build a shelter.

In today's world, our brains are still wired to find pleasure in different pursuits. Your brain might generate a large reward response when you engage in computer games. This leads to you feeling strong urges to play repeatedly, ultimately leading to a gaming disorder, whilst I can play a computer game and find it enjoyable but not highly rewarding. On the other hand, I might have a drink of alcohol, find it hugely rewarding and immediately want another, while you enjoy a drink but don't feel the same strong urge for the next round.

Many addiction experts will tell you that most people today have some form of addiction. It comes down to how much of a problem their *drug* and level of dependence create that determines whether they seek a way to overcome it. We all have the propensity to develop an addiction, and—let's face it—more people are addicted to smartphones and other devices now than ever (but I think there are already plenty of books on that topic!).

The brain evolved to develop the ability to pursue rewarding behaviours for a powerful reason. That reason is survival. It just never meant for those rewarding behaviours to be the easily accessible and extremely rewarding substances and behaviours so widely available to us today.

There are other factors that make some people more vulnerable to develop an addiction. These include sociocultural factors, availability of their *drug* and ease of access, stress or trauma history, as well as factors like a person's age when they first engage with the *drug*. These fall outside this discussion, but several are referred to within some of the other chapters as they relate to eating disorders.

• • • ● • ● • • •

# The Evolutionary Theory to Restrictive Eating Disorders: Adapted–Flee–From–Famine

When you understand that our brains have evolved to find reward from survival-based behaviours such as seeking and eating food, having shelter and being warm, it makes restrictive eating disorders appear even more illogical from an evolutionary perspective.

Why would the brain of someone with a restrictive eating disorder have evolved to find reward in not eating, exercising to the point of collapse or other behaviours that result in their becoming malnourished?

A normal brain finds pleasure in food, and this triggers dopamine release, motivating a person to continue eating because food is essential for survival. Most people who attempt diets will find that at some point their brain and body take over and drive them to eat so that they stay sufficiently nourished. So, what has happened in the brain of someone with an eating disorder in which there is the opposite response? Was there a time in evolution that these behaviours, which on the surface look like deliberate self-starvation, were ever helpful?

Many of you will already be familiar with the flee-from-famine evolutionary theory of eating disorders[1]. This theory explains why some brains have evolved to pursue food restriction and high levels of movement when it perceives that less food is available in the immediate environment.

For those who are less familiar with this evolutionary theory, an explanation is given below. If you want to know more about it, look up the work of Dr Shan Guisinger, who has written extensively on the topic.

In a nutshell, the adapted-flee-from-famine theory hypothesises that the typical symptoms of a restrictive eating disorder—which include restricting food intake, hyperactivity and denial of a problem—are evolved mechanisms that allowed certain of our ancestors who were *nomadic foragers* to leave depleted environments in search of food. Today, those of us with the genetic blueprint for this adaptation response to famine can trigger our brain into these behaviours if we lose too much weight and enter a state of sufficient energy deficit. This weight loss might initially arise from engaging in dieting behaviours or overexercising due to today's cultural expectations. It can also come from a physical illness that causes weight loss or from other factors that cause a person to stop eating or to enter a state of prolonged energy deficit.

Our nomadic forager ancestors often found themselves in environments of low food availability. They needed to be able to move locations to find food for themselves and their tribe. A normal physiological response to low food intake is to preserve energy by reducing someone's drive to move and increasing their hunger so that they rest and eat to restore. However, this response is not beneficial to someone if they need to migrate from their scarce environment to find a place with dense food availability for survival. In this situation, it's beneficial for a starving forager to be able to stop foraging and eating the depleted resources locally and to feel restless and energetic so they can move to find food. As well as this, there is additional benefit to them not being able to recognise how dangerously malnourished they are. Within the flee-from-famine theory, there are three key adaptations that have been identified to help escape a famine situation and ultimately survive: the ability to ignore food immediately available, hyperactivity and denial of starvation symptoms with distorted body image.

Within this framework it would be key for survival if compulsions to move and avoid food were experienced as more urgent than other human needs.

This evolutionary theory explains why people with restrictive eating disorders come from a wide variety of social and cultural backgrounds and life histories, with different reasons for the initial weight loss that triggered the eating disorder. It also provides a rationale for why some other animals also develop typical eating disorder symptoms, such as hyperactivity and food avoidance when they are starved.

It's important to also understand that not every person in our ancestors' tribe would have had the genetic predisposition for this adaptive response to a famine situation. The theory is that those who did were the minority in their groups, but they were the individuals who would have had the drive and stamina to migrate even though malnourished. They will have had a powerful aversion to any behaviours that could lead to energy surplus because this would have switched off the migratory response and not been helpful for survival. At the end of the day, it was these individuals and their optimism and energy who inspired the others in their tribe to continue migrating so they could all reach a new hunting and gathering ground.

The need to inspire others in the tribe is another characteristic from the evolutionary theory that also links to a key feature many with restrictive eating disorders experience: *martyr complex*. Many people with restrictive eating disorders develop an inner belief that their behaviours are the right choice, even looking down on people who are not as *in control* of their own eating or who don't exercise as much and live in bigger bodies. Some with eating disorders even seek out ways to inspire others and lead by example when it comes to their pursuits of weight control. Examples of this are when people with restrictive eating disorders enter professions in fitness or nutritional guidance. A lot of people with eating disorders won't admit to this inner experience of *martyrdom* because they fear being considered arrogant or self-important. However, from an evolutionary perspective, this feature of restrictive eating disorders was clearly a benefit. For our ancestor, it was crucial to be able to inspire the rest of their tribe to summon the little energy they still had, ignore their hunger and follow along to find a richer foraging ground. For this, self-belief that what they were doing was the right thing and that others should follow suit was an asset. Their ability to win the trust of the rest of the tribe would have been at risk if they were seen to be hesitant. There is more information about martyr complex in the next section.

In the times of our ancestors, the necessary characteristics required to drive them to migrate and motivate the tribe to follow would have been switched on for a relatively short time—that is, until a more abundant environment was found. Once in an environment with plenty of food sources again, the social pressure and support from family and friends would have encouraged our ancestor to start eating. This in turn reversed their energy deficit state and switched off the migratory response and related behaviours. Because the migratory behaviours had only persisted for a relatively short time, there was minimal risk of our ancestor developing deeply entrenched brain circuitry that was highly resistant to change. Instead, support to eat again would have reactivated the circuits in their brain driving *normal* eating, which had not had time to break down, and so the migratory response subsided.

When you consider what's happening in the brain, the evolutionary theory to restrictive eating disorders ties in with the addiction model.

For those with the genetic blueprint to *flee from famine* or, as we know it today, to develop a restrictive eating disorder, the brain is primed to make key changes if a person enters a state of energy deficit. When the brain notices that the body's fat and lean tissue stores have fallen below a certain point, it will switch on the adaptive migratory famine response. This involves a high reward response to food avoidance behaviours, movement and exercise and other behaviours that sustain energy deficit. The brain will also promote and reward thoughts that prevent the person from recognising their hunger or how malnourished they are and stimulate an avoidant response to weight gain. The brain achieves this with the same processes as the addictive model discussed in Chapter 3—by using the body's natural opiates and dopamine to reward and drive the behaviours.

In someone with an eating disorder today, these behaviours last much longer than they would have done in our ancestors' time, and so the brain continues to reward and motivate these behaviours for what can be years or decades. This leads to the development of the deeply wired-in brain circuitry that causes these behaviours to become embedded habits and to the significant dopamine deficit people then develop. In addition, the numbing effects of the addictive nature of the eating disorder becomes a strong maintaining factor, making it even more painful and very difficult to stop. All this together leads to the brain having developed the entrenched addiction to energy deficit that people with eating disorders experience today.

The other factor in our modern times that makes overcoming this evolutionary phenomenon more complicated relates to the beliefs that underlie the behaviours. Our ancestors would have understood why they needed to keep moving without stopping to eat in the scarce environment they were in. The compulsions to migrate and lead others to do the same made sense to them and their tribe. When they found a dense foraging ground, stopping to eat again would have been logical and hence easier to pursue. Today, people believe that they are engaging in compelling energy-deficit-creating behaviours because they have a *fear of weight gain* or want to fit a societal norm. Perhaps they fear being *unhealthy* or becoming *obese* due to public health messages that often do more harm than good. For people today then, not only have their behaviours lasted longer and become more embedded than they were in our ancestors' time, but they also are driven by powerful, ongoing beliefs. This aspect of eating disorders and overcoming one is discussed in more detail later (see Chapter 11, *What About Fear of Weight Gain?*).

It's helpful to understand the evolutionary theories to addictions and eating disorders because they can help you make sense of behaviours or *illnesses* that in today's world seem inexplicable, which only adds to a self-perception of being *a bit crazy.* At one point in history, these brain system changes served a real purpose for survival. Today they form addictions that can ruin lives.

To me, the evolutionary theory to eating disorders makes more sense than anything else and takes the concept of *mental illness* or a *diseased brain* to what is in fact a very clever brain doing what was once essential for survival.

I hope that as you form a greater understanding of this evolutionary theory, it will help you to reflect in a new light on the compulsions that form part of the eating disorder for you. This can help you understand why you need to overcome the strong urges to pursue energy deficit and instead eat large amounts of food so that your brain can trust that it's now in an environment that is a dense foraging ground.

# Martyr Complex Within Restrictive Eating Disorders

The evolutionary theory to restrictive eating disorders explains why a strong drive to inspire others is a common feature of a restrictive eating disorder. In a famine situation, our ancestor—with symptoms and traits that we today consider to be an eating disorder—would have been the one to rally his starving tribe and motivate them to keep walking to find a new foraging ground with abundant supplies of food. The ability to inspire others and an inner sense of righteousness were necessary traits that would help to win the trust of the tribe and encourage them to follow. For our ancestors, survival of their tribe was dependent on this ability to inspire.

Today, despite there no longer being any survival-based need for these traits, they remain features commonly seen in people with eating disorders. The drive to inspire and an inner sense of superiority that people with restrictive eating disorders often experience can be considered a form of *martyr complex*.

*Martyr complex* is a term used to describe people who seek out the feeling of being a martyr, putting others' needs above their own suffering to give their life meaning. Someone who has a martyr complex is often identified by those around them as being helpful and agreeable. They are seen to sacrifice anything, including their own health, to help others.

From the Middle Ages there are documented reports of *starving saints* in Europe. These were women, often Catholic nuns, who were observed to starve themselves in extreme ways. They claimed to be doing so to communicate with Christ by imitating the suffering of Jesus.

The term used to describe the self-starvation seen in these women was *anorexia mirabilis*. These women are some of the earliest documented cases of people with what we consider to be eating disorders today. The nuns starved themselves, claiming that it was for the greater good and that they felt their suffering was of little consequence to the bigger picture. For these women, the drive to inspire others, which is so commonly seen in eating disorders, appeared to manifest through a deeply held belief that their actions were pure and right.

Today we rarely hear about people with eating disorders suppressing their body weight for reasons of religion, but the concept of martyr syndrome is still very present, although often overlooked.

People with restrictive eating disorders are excellent at convincing both themselves and those around them that the behaviours they engage in are healthy and worthy of praise and recognition, when in reality they are driven by a powerful addiction to energy deficit.

We live in a culture today in which eating restrictively, exercising and being thin or slim is highly esteemed, no matter that the cause is a restrictive eating disorder. This means that people are very often praised for having a dangerous addiction that is ruining their lives.

Another symptom of a restrictive eating disorder is a false sense of high energy and of being superhuman. This makes people with restrictive eating disorders more convinced that they are healthy and capable, which strengthens their self-denial of having a problem. The urge they experience to constantly move also creates a drive to keep busy, which leads to others identifying them as someone who is always productive and on the go—another thing our culture praises, even when it's damaging.

The positive recognition people receive for behaviours that are symptoms of the eating disorder gives rise to an even greater sense of internal reward, which further reinforces their martyr complex.

Some other common examples of how martyr complex can be reinforced in people with restrictive eating disorders are:

- Receiving praise for *being good* when they say no to the slice of cake or turn down the side of fries;

- Being celebrated for their compulsive exercise, rather than it being recognised as a dangerous addiction;

- Receiving compliments for being thin, slim or for weight loss;

- Earning recognition from colleagues or employers as someone who always takes on more work and performs to a high level; and

- Always being the one to do the cleaning, washing up, cooking or walking the dog and lovingly teased by family and friends as being *house-proud* and incapable of sitting down.

In this way, people inadvertently receive praise for having dangerous eating disorders, which gives them an internal sense of reward and feelings of self-pride and self-righteousness.

It's also not uncommon for martyr complex to result in a drive to inspire others in more formal ways. This is when people with restrictive eating disorders take on professions as fitness instructors, helping others to get fit or lose weight. Some train to become dieticians or nutritionists to *teach* others how and what to eat. These career choices are rarely made before the person develops the eating disorder and purely arise from it. These examples are not given here as a judgment on anyone who has made these career choices. Eating disorders create a powerful drive to inspire others and a strong self-belief that what you are doing and teaching to others is right at the time you are doing so.

Martyr complex is a dangerous part of a restrictive eating disorder. When someone feels virtuous for continuing to pursue damaging, addictive behaviours, it's a significant hindrance to their ability to recognise the harm in their actions and overcome them. The praise received in the pursuit to inspire others perpetuates the self-denial that they have a problem.

Martyr complex needs recognition for how detrimental it can be. For those of you with an eating disorder, it's time to face reality. Your workouts are not praiseworthy. Your below-set-point weight is not healthy and is not something anyone should envy. When you refuse food, it's not you *being good*; it's your brain getting another fix from the pursuit of energy deficit. Your continuing drive to work, study, be superhuman, volunteer and save the world merely distracts you from dealing with the eating disorder head-on, and it's unhealthy and dangerous. This is not something anyone should be encouraging.

The sense of being superhuman you experience when in a state of energy deficit is a lie. It's a key feature of a restrictive eating disorder and something that hides just how malnourished you are. If people around you knew the truth, their perception of what they observe in you would quickly change.

Continuing to live in a way that is damaging your health and prevents you from overcoming the addictive behaviours that drive the eating disorder needs to stop. The process of overcoming the eating disorder will create feelings of guilt and wrongdoing, but when you experience these, reassure yourself that you are doing the right thing. It's these brave and selfless actions that are most definitely worthy of praise and respect.

---

1. Guisinger, S. (2003). Adapted to flee famine: Adding an evolutionary perspective on anorexia nervosa. Psychological Review, 110(4), 745-761. https://doi.org/10.1037/0033-2 95X.110.4.745.

# Chapter Eight

---

# Genetics & Cultural Risk Factors

## The Genetic Link to Eating Disorders

In the last few years, researchers have made a big push to discover more about the genetic link to eating disorders. In 2019, a study was published that has collected samples from nearly 17,000 people with anorexia nervosa and over 55,000 controls from seventeen countries. This has provided some of the best indication yet about where the genetic links to anorexia are to be found.

The Eating Disorder Genetic Initiative (EDGI) continues to run from various parts of the world and is still seeking more people to take part. They are also now expanding their focus from anorexia to other eating disorder subtypes, and they aim to recruit much more inclusively, seeking populations that give a wide diversity of race, age, gender, sex, ethnicity and body shape and size[1].

The research findings that have been published to date are largely in relation to people with the anorexia nervosa (AN) subtype. Eight genetic loci that have direct links to AN have been discovered. The current findings have also found a strong genetic link between AN and obsessive-compulsive disorder (OCD), as well as to anxiety and depression.

It's important to understand that there is not just one gene for an eating disorder and if you don't have it, then your risk is minimal. As with other mental and physical illnesses and many human traits, there are several genes that contribute. The eight that have been found are thought to be a scratch on the surface in relation to how many genetic loci exist that will contribute to an eating disorder. An individual's likelihood of developing an eating disorder comes down to their overall genetic makeup (also referred to as genetic blueprint).

A talk given in 2022 by Professor Gerome Breen, one of the leading researchers for the UK EDGI study, presented their most recent findings, which are beginning to account for other eating disorders beyond AN. Their findings suggest that eating disorders overall have a 40–65 percent genetic risk, implying that environmental or other factors make up the rest of the risk. For people with AN, the genetic risk is 50–60 percent, while for binge eating disorder (BED), it's slightly lower at 40–50 percent. Researchers also report that people with the most severe symptoms and longest duration of illness have a higher genetic load (meaning they have more genetic loci linked to eating disorders).

## What Environmental Factors Could 'Switch On' the Genes for an Eating Disorder?

Somebody can have a genetic blueprint that will make them susceptible to an eating disorder but never develop one. Genes need to be activated for them to express and present, which means the person then develops the condition. This activation is often an environmental factor—something external that tells the body that this particular set of behaviours or this trait is needed right now.

The science regarding eating disorder genetics is very much in its infancy. Knowing exactly what factors can cause eating disorder genes to activate remains uncertain. However, some studies do exist, largely carried out on mice and other animals, which provide some clues.

For the last couple of decades, repeated studies of mice and rat populations have demonstrated time and again that when the animal's food availability is restricted and it's given a running wheel, the rodent will start running and running and become food avoidant, displaying typical symptoms of a restrictive eating disorder. This has led to the conclusion that food restriction—i.e., energy deficit—is a key risk factor for restrictive eating disorder development[2]. These early studies did not account for genetics.

A more recent study with some potentially significant findings was carried out on mice that had certain genes known to be related to AN. This study is important because it accounted for the specific AN gene in the mice being studied, alongside environmental changes. The mice with a specific AN gene were subjected to a restricted food intake and isolated to increase their stress levels. The results showed that mice subjected to both of these environmental changes developed symptoms of ongoing food avoidance and typical AN behaviours. The mice that were allowed to live happily with as much food as they wanted and lots of friends did not develop AN, and those with only food restriction or social isolation as a single environmental change also failed to show development of AN. Therefore, this study indicates that it's both restricted food intake or energy deficit and some form of stress which triggers the activation of the genes and the development of the eating disorder. The researchers speculated that in humans a simple perceived pressure to lose weight could be sufficient as the contributing stress factor[3].

Overall, recent research is clearly indicating that eating disorders have a strong genetic contribution and that genes are *activated* by entering a state of energy deficit with or without some form of additional stress. The energy deficit can arise from any number of causes. The stress component could simply come from social pressure or from a life change such as starting a new job, going to university or having a child. For some it will arise from a more significant trauma. Where this is the case, it's important to understand that the traumatic event didn't cause the eating disorder. It was one significant factor—in addition to entering a state of energy deficit—that activated genetic susceptibility.

## What Does the Genetic Link to Eating Disorders Mean for You?

It can be frightening to think you might be carrying DNA that you can pass on to your future generations. Perhaps you are a parent of a child with an eating disorder, and you are now feeling guilt that you might have given them a genetic blueprint leading to their disorder. At the end of the day, genetics play a part in most of the conditions we can get in our life span, as well as our personality traits. It would have been strange if the genome studies had not found genes that contribute to an eating disorder (unless you believe the stereotypical view that eating disorders are merely teenage girls being deliberately difficult!). The risk of a person developing an eating disorder will come down to a combination of factors, including genetics and environmental contributions, and perhaps chance. If you have children or plan to have children in the future, there might well be aspects of their genetic blueprint that will increase their risk of developing an eating disorder in their lifetime. However, this does not mean they will develop one. As with any condition, all we can do is take steps to prevent them, whether we have a familial history or not. For eating disorders, this means promoting a good relationship with food and our body to reduce the risks of typical eating disorder behaviours being engaged in in the first instance.

The benefits of these genetic findings today and locating the specific range of genetic loci that can contribute to an eating disorder are that they provide much more information about the biology of eating disorders. It's hoped that this will help professionals and scientists understand the condition better, and this then can help inform how to treat and address them.

The other positive aspect of the recent genetic findings is that they are pushing health professionals and scientists into taking eating disorders more seriously. The ongoing stigma of eating disorders cannot continue with these new findings, and perhaps this will lead to better funding, more research and in time (let's hope), far more effective management of eating disorders.

### Linking Genetic and Environmental Risks to the Evolutionary Theory of Eating Disorders

If you refer back to the evolutionary theory of eating disorders and link this to these genetic findings, you can begin to understand why these genes would have evolved. Our ancestors who were facing scarce environments needed to be able to limit their food intake and feel hyperactive so they could migrate. For these ancestors, it would have been beneficial if their decreased food intake, combined with an increase in stress—because the imminent inability to feed your family is stressful—led to the activation of genes that made it more possible for them to migrate on very limited intake. The people with these genes were the ones who could get up and move, seek a new foraging ground and inspire their family and friends to follow them.

The genes that put people at risk of developing an eating disorder might seem like an unhappy fate of nature today. However, to those ancestors of ours, they represented an ability to not just survive on an individual level but also ensure survival of their tribe.

If you are interested in taking part in the genetic EDGI study, please visit this website: https://edgiuk.org/international-sites/

•  •  •  ●•  ●  •  •  •

# Addressing the Stereotypes

## Eating Disorders Through the Ages

In the last few decades, eating disorders have largely been attributed to being an *emotional imbalance* in young women, stemming from a societal pressure to be thin. Alongside this, the blame has been inflicted on dysfunctional families. The stereotype of a teenage girl with anorexia who is white, middle class and perfectionistic with controlling parents was a picture many health professionals upheld. The professionals who were in roles of supporting and treating people with eating disorders were predominantly of the view that eating disorders grew from a culture in which you can never be too thin.

Assuming this is the case, then how do we explain the fact that eating disorders have been around for centuries?

The first reported cases of what sounds very much like restrictive eating disorders date from the twelfth and thirteenth centuries. These early reported cases come from the fasting saints, who claimed not eating was a spiritual act to demonstrate a devout commitment to God. These women also glorified the starvation process, seeking a sense of martyrdom. In the sixteenth century, women displaying symptoms of anorexia were considered witches. In 1689, Richard Morton, an English physician, provided the first medical description of anorexia symptoms, which he labelled as *nervous consumption.* In the seventeenth through nineteenth centuries, there are descriptions of *wasting disease,* and in the early twentieth century, restrictive eating disorders were considered endocrine disorders. In the early twentieth century, there was the first push to remove children with eating disorders from their parents, blaming the parents for their child's condition. It was then in the 1930s and '40s that restrictive eating disorders were first referred to as psychological conditions. Descriptions of bulimia also date from medieval times where there are reports of the wealthy making themselves vomit during meals so that they could eat more. In 1903, a physician, Pierre Janet, observed patients with purging behaviours typical of bulimia in his works. Descriptions of binge eating disorder can also be found in historical literature, though it was only in 1959 that the first formal reports on binge eating disorder can be found.

Therefore, if clear cases of eating disorders have been reported for centuries, and cases before the 1960s and '70s were never attributed to a pressure to be thin because this was not a cultural pressure before then, why do restrictive eating disorders today have this stereotype?

It's time to face reality. Eating disorders affect people from all walks of life, and they don't discriminate by gender, age, race, social class or anything else.

## Eating Disorders Do Not Only Start in Adolescence

The stereotypical belief surrounding restrictive eating disorders is that they start in adolescence.

A large UK study of over 9,000 participants found that 57 percent of people with AN, 52 percent with binge eating and 39 percent of people with BN first have symptoms when they are older than eighteen years. There were far fewer males in the sample than females, but in males, adult onset (over the age of twenty-five years) was more common than in females. Conversely, so, too, was the onset of AN in males under the age of ten years. The study also included participants with an age of eating disorder onset in their fifties, sixties and seventies[4].

When you consider these findings, it's also important to remember that these are from populations of people who have an eating disorder diagnosis. Many people from more diverse groups, including those over the age of forty years, are left undiagnosed because eating disorders are not considered by health professionals in these older age groups. Therefore, the reality of how many people develop eating disorders later in life is likely to be much greater than these figures depict.

## Restrictive Eating Disorders Affect People of All Body Sizes

People have been fighting for years for recognition of the fact that eating disorders, including AN, can and do occur in people of all body shapes and sizes. The view that AN is only present in someone of a below *normal* range BMI is, thankfully, gradually becoming discredited. There is now the entry into the Diagnostic Statistics Manual of *atypical anorexia*. This is classified as a person showing all the signs and symptoms of AN, but, *despite significant weight loss, their weight is within or above the normal range*. This is some progress. Before 2013, there was no recognition in the DSM for people with AN in bodies that were above a BMI of seventeen.

This meant that anyone with AN who presented to their health professional and did not fit the weight criteria wouldn't have received a diagnosis and therefore no treatment. However, even now that *atypical* AN is recognised in the DSM, people in bigger bodies who do seek help have symptoms for a longer period and a greater level of weight loss before they get diagnosed. They are also much less likely to be offered intensive treatment.

Is it any wonder that for years, eating disorder services or health professionals have left people feeling that they need to lose more weight to *justify* the help they are desperate for?

Finally, researchers are providing the evidence needed that means that eating disorder treatment providers must now recognise that eating disorders with all the same AN symptoms and risks can and do occur in people of all sizes.

A large study published in the highly esteemed *Nature* journal in 2022[5] has concluded that people with all the symptoms of AN but who have a higher genetically determined BMI (set point weight) may be under-diagnosed with the current diagnostic criteria. The study called for a move away from body weight being a diagnostic criterion for AN. Medical complications from AN are similar in people regardless of how much weight they lose, and it's known that length of illness is a better predictor for how entrenched an eating disorder is, not body weight. Any weight suppression of even 5 percent below a person's genetic set weight range is clinically significant in terms of the medical complications it can create.

Eating disorder professionals have been slow to listen to the general eating disorder community and to hear the changes they have been calling on for years—primarily removing BMI as a criteria for treatment. This is why recent publications such as the one in the *Nature* journal are so important, as they provide the research evidence required to back up this call for change. The medical communities cannot continue to fail to notice, diagnose and support people with very real restrictive eating disorder symptoms who are in *normal or higher weight* bodies for much longer.

### Eating Disorders Affect People of All Genders and Sexual Orientations

Eating disorders are stereotypically ascribed as affecting women and girls only. This has been compounded by treatment services that are set up to predominantly support females (one eating disorder unit I spent time in had fourteen inpatient beds of which only one could be offered to a male patient). Research and even diagnostic criteria for eating disorders have also over-whelmingly focused on females and rarely males.

Despite this, we know that eating disorders do affect people from all genders and across the spectra of sexual orientation. As with people in larger bodies, if a person with an eating disorder does not fit the stereotypical picture, and treatment services are not set up to meet their needs, they are much less likely to come forward to get a formal diagnosis or receive help. Health professionals are also significantly less likely to even consider an eating disorder diagnosis in males than in females.

According to current statistics, the gender ratio of females to males is 7:1 for an AN diagnosis, 3.2:1 for BN and for 2.8:1 for BED[6]. As males are less likely to be diagnosed, these statistics are undoubtedly a long way from the true picture.

When it comes to sexual orientation, there is thought to be a higher prevalence of eating disorders diagnosed in LGBTQIA+ individuals. A range of theories exist for why this might be the case. These theories predominantly come down to environmental rather than genetic risk factors, but there's still a lot that's unknown.

The indisputable truth is that eating disorders affect people from across the gender and sexual orientation spectra. There is now a drive within eating disorder research to ensure that future studies into eating disorders include individuals from both sexes, all genders and all sexualities. This will be an important step towards making anyone with an eating disorder feel more comfortable to come forward for help and recognised by health professionals.

## Eating Disorders Affect People of all Races and Ethnicities

Eating disorders affect people from all races and ethnicities. However, the current research data available to back up this statement is limited because most large population-based studies of eating disorders have been carried out in the US, Europe and Australia. There are very few studies from Asia or Africa.

Interestingly, though, studies that do exist across a diverse range of races and ethnicities show that the most common symptoms of eating disorders differ depending on race or ethnicity.

Asian men and women with restrictive eating disorders report far less *fear of fatness* (which is a key diagnostic criterion within the DSM-5) compared to Europeans, Americans and African Americans. This will impact on the prevalence statistics from these groups if they aren't receiving an official diagnosis because they don't meet the full requirements of the DSM criteria.

In my view, it makes sense that people from cultures in which the thin ideal is not so widespread don't attribute their otherwise typical eating disorder symptoms to a fear of fatness or drive to be thin. As I discuss in Chapter II, I believe that the *fear of fatness* explanation so often attributed to restrictive eating disorders is an explanation that's convenient in our modern Western culture. If we look to wider populations where being thin is not a cultural pressure, it becomes clear that another explanation is needed for what drives the behaviours seen in people with restrictive eating disorders. Could it be that a more likely explanation is a neurobiological addiction to energy deficit that can be explained in simple evolutionary terms?

As with others who don't fit the typical picture, people from non-white or non-Western races and cultures can be overlooked by health professionals, and they are less likely to seek treatment. As more research studies are carried out into populations from all races and ethnicities, perhaps treatment and diagnostic practices will become more inclusive, and the health disparities that exist now will be broken down.

## Eating Disorders Affect People from All Socioeconomic Backgrounds

Restrictive eating disorders are stereotypically considered to predominantly affect people from middle or upper socioeconomic groups. Recent studies, however, show that this is not the case and that eating disorders affect people from all socioeconomic status levels. Despite this, those from lower levels are less likely to be screened or offered treatment for eating disorders.

There are also some studies today coming out of the US which show that individuals of lower economic backgrounds who have food insecurity and insufficiency are more likely to develop eating disorders. This would tie into the evolutionary theory of eating disorders and to the research evidence indicating that a genetic susceptibility to an eating disorder is very likely switched on by a restricted food intake—further discrediting the view that eating disorders are predominantly related to a fear of weight gain.

## Eating Disorders Affect People Without Significant Life Problems or Past Trauma

In recent decades eating disorders have also been *psychologised* and considered to be downstream issues resulting to other problems in a person's life or past trauma. But this isn't a necessary factor in determining who develops an eating disorder. Someone can have a perfect life and still develop an eating disorder, as they can with other forms of addiction. For some, the eating disorder might even develop when their life is going extremely well in every other way. The key risk factors, as discussed earlier, to develop a restrictive eating disorder are to enter a state of energy deficit and a genetic susceptibility. Some form of life stress might be a risk factor, but the jury is still out on that one. However, even if life stress is a key risk factor, it's thought this stress could be as simple as a perceived social pressure to lose weight.

When it comes to eating disorders, the reality is that a person can have a great childhood, a good life now, wonderful parents, a supportive partner, a good career and perfect children and yet still develop an eating disorder. So many will have experienced being asked by well-meaning people, *Why did you develop an eating disorder? What caused it?*

There doesn't need to be a stressful or traumatic life cause. It can be as simple as a combination of insufficient energy intake to the body's needs and an unlucky genetic blueprint.

It's understandable why this stereotype of eating disorders persists. As humans, we are natural-born storytellers, and when something as seemingly irrational as an eating disorder exists, we want to create a story as to why it's happening and what's causing it. This need to psychoanalyse also stems from the desire to treat, usually through therapy. Yet sometimes eating disorders cannot be rationalised with powerful stories about unhappy lives or past trauma for which the only solution the person could find came from an eating disorder. A lot of people do have depression and anxiety with eating disorders and other forms of addiction, but this is just as likely to be a result of the addictive disorder, not the cause of it.

Of course, some people do have past trauma and other life issues that contributed to their developing an eating disorder and that are now a definite factor in maintaining it. Some people live in isolation, which can be another key component. Eating disorders are powerful at numbing and helping to block out emotional pain or difficult memories. Therefore, for anyone who does have past trauma or other significant forms of life stress, addressing them will be critical to successfully moving through the pain and overcoming an eating disorder. To achieve this, therapy or other forms of professional support will be needed.

Eating disorders can affect people with no significant life problems or past trauma, and it should not be assumed that an eating disorder developed from a need to control one's life or a need for perfectionism. These stereotypical views need to be broken down. Where they do persist, people with happy lives who develop an eating disorder are left digging for something that must have *caused* it, when there was no unhappy life cause.

### To Summarise

The all too commonly held view of restrictive eating disorders as a teenage girl striving to be thin due to peer pressure is damaging. It discredits all those with restrictive eating disorders who are not female, white, rich, middle class, teenagers, in thin or slim bodies and who come from stable family homes or relationships.

Health professionals fail to identify eating disorders in diverse groups because they are not looking for them. Services are not created to support individuals who are older, male, in bigger bodies or from diverse cultures. At the same time, those with eating disorders who don't fit the stereotype either fail to recognise what is happening to them or, if they do, resist seeking help and support for fear of being belittled or not being believed.

In addition, people from diverse groups are omitted from research. This means that the available evidence and science around eating disorders—which play such an important part in informing treatment guidelines and health professionals' understanding—are biased.

Changes are being made. There are steps of movement in the right direction but let's just hope, for the sake of so many people who aren't being recognised but who have damaging eating disorders today, that these much-needed changes are expedited.

In the meantime, perhaps by educating yourself as to what the risk factors to developing an eating disorder are, who is truly affected and what overcoming one takes, you can inform and enlighten those people in a position to help you.

• • • ●•● • • •

# Social & Cultural Risk Factors for Restrictive Eating Disorders

### Western Diet Culture Makes Ease of Access to the *Drug* of Energy Deficit a Powerful Risk Factor

The genetic link to eating disorders was explained at the beginning of this chapter. This included the current understanding from recent research that many people who develop eating disorders do so as a result of a genetic susceptibility. The relevant genes can be *switched on* by certain environmental triggers so that they express and give rise to the commonly seen eating disorder symptoms and compulsive habits. The key environmental factors that will activate this genetic susceptibility are entering a state of prolonged energy deficit, with or without some form of stress.

Today, eating disorders are known to be on the rise, as are most other forms of addiction, perhaps due to a combination of our high-pressured culture and easy access to *instant fixes* (hello smartphone!).

One of the biggest risk factors to developing and maintaining any addiction is the ease of access someone has to the substance or behaviour they develop the addiction to. For restrictive eating disorders, not only is ease of access greater than ever when it comes to information about how to pursue the *drug* of energy deficit, but so, too, is the encouragement to pursue it.

In the Western world, our culture is such that dieting behaviours are applauded, and information about how to eat restrictively or lose weight is commonplace. Weight loss information is found in our health centres, the adverts we are bombarded with, the news media and Internet. Terrifyingly, these weight loss messages today are also commonly given in our schools. Exercise is actively encouraged with a *you can't do too much* attitude, as is restrictive eating.

For people with eating disorders or those who have a genetic susceptibility, the encouragement towards and ease of access to that first taste of the *drug* of energy deficit is higher than it ever has been. Online influencers who promote a certain body type, dieting behaviours or fitness extremes and portray a false picture of *a perfect life* pull people into following them. Vulnerable people, fed up with their current lives, are lured into the belief that if they eat and work out in the same way as the influencers they aspire to, they, too, will achieve that life. For people who decide they want to lose weight, a simple Google search will enable them to access every kind of restrictive diet and other weight loss tool there is, all at the click of a button. This kind of instantly available Internet information wasn't available two to three decades ago in the way it is now.

The other key factor in today's culture, pushing more towards dieting behaviours, comes directly from our governments, health professionals and even our schools. The powerful diet industry, which has enough money to buy influence over national and international policy makers, has managed to create so much noise about the dangers of the *obesity epidemic* that the encouragement to engage in energy–deficit–creating behaviours is everywhere. These messages impact everyone irrespective of their age, race, gender or even their current body size.

For anyone with a susceptibility to develop an eating disorder, these constant messages and easy access to information about how to lose weight are significant risk factors. Those who fall prey to these messages and decide to pursue an innocent weight loss journey won't realise until it's too late the life–changing consequences these behaviours will have on them. Initially engaging in behaviours that create a state of energy deficit will be highly rewarding to their brain, which will motivate them to repeat the behaviours. In this way, it's instantly reinforcing and quickly becomes habitual. Even when any original intention there had been to diet has gone and the behaviours are now clearly detrimental, their addictively seductive and compelling nature makes them incredibly difficult to stop because the eating disorder has taken hold.

### Social Groups as a Risk Factor

Another significant risk factor as to whether someone develops an eating disorder or other form of addiction comes from the social groups they belong to.

The community you move and live within and the people around you can impact whether you start to engage in the *drug* and continue to pursue it. We often think of peer pressure as a concept that applies more to children and adolescents, and perhaps they are more vulnerable to it. However, adults are also susceptible to social influence and peer pressure.

Humans are social animals. Connection to others is important, and we want to be liked by those around us, which often means that we try to fit in. We try to be the same as others so they will like us. Therefore, if a social group or community we are part of typically engages in a particular behaviour or uses substances that can create dependence, it's more likely that we will engage in it too.

Consider city workers who live fast-paced lives and where recreational drug use can be commonplace. They have systems in place to ensure easy access to those drugs, and there is a clear element of social pressure to take them recreationally as a way to *let off steam* or perhaps *celebrate a win*. For some, that initial recreational use becomes habitual and addictive.

Online gamers form communities with other gamers, giving them much-needed connection. This creates a desire for more engagement with the online gaming world, which ultimately becomes addictive.

For people with eating disorders or with a susceptibility to develop one, it isn't hard in our current culture to find themselves part of a social group that supports and encourages typical behaviours of a restrictive eating disorder. Their friendship groups might include others who are very body focused and talk a lot about diets, weight loss or fitness. They might belong to sports clubs, gyms or similar communities that encourage the ongoing pursuit of exercise to be leaner or lose weight. This can be a clear route into an eating disorder for anyone vulnerable to the risks of energy deficit and in whom these behaviours can quickly escalate into compulsions that become incredibly hard to stop.

### Why Are Children and Teenagers More Vulnerable to Developing an Eating Disorder?

People ask why restrictive eating disorders appear to be on the rise in teenagers and even preteens. This question is easy to answer.

Children today are being actively educated in our schools about how to follow restrictive diets. They are taught that *fat is bad*, and they are given messages every single day that come from diet industry propaganda. As if this wasn't dangerous enough, the young people who are sensitive to these messages and decide to pursue them don't need to recruit the help of an adult in order to do so. Instead, they have access to social media influencers and online information about how to eat *healthily* or lose weight in potentially dangerous or extreme ways. Their first taste of the *drug* of energy deficit is encouraged by their responsible adults and possibly even applauded. The ability to learn how to pursue it with even greater intensity is then freely available at the click of a button from their own bedrooms.

When it comes to teenagers and young people, ease of access to this information is even more damaging because the brain of a young person is still so plastic and easily influenced by new learning.

In the teenage brain, connections between their neurons form and reform with relative ease, which can give rise to the development of new behaviours and deep learning more quickly and easily than in a less plastic adult brain. Therefore, the teenage brain holds huge learning potential but also has a greater degree of vulnerability. Coupled with this, the prefrontal cortex of a teenager is slower to mature, so the ability to apply reason, judgment and impulse control is much lower than in adults. This makes a young person more prone to follow behaviours that result from their emotions and on impulse. At the same time, pleasure circuits in teenagers are much higher, so the rewards they feel from first engaging in a potentially addictive behaviour will be extremely pleasurable and enticing to repeat, causing their brains to wire in these new behaviours even faster.

Peer groups and social pressure become much more important to young people in these age groups as they begin to move away from close parental relationships. They are then more likely to pursue rewarding behaviours or habits that they perceive as necessary to fit in.

When a child or adolescent has such a highly adaptable brain—coupled with pressure towards weight-controlling behaviours and ease of access to information about how to pursue this—it's unsurprising that young people with the susceptibility to develop an eating disorder are more vulnerable than ever.

## To Summarise

The ease of access to energy deficit as a *drug* today is higher than it has ever been in our history. Media and government messages and the huge availability of information in all kinds of formats are teaching people where to find their *drug* and how to pursue it—promising them a better life if they do and applauding them for it.

Social groups often support and encourage energy-deficit-creating behaviours, adding to the risks of developing a restrictive eating disorder or making it harder to overcome one.

When someone has an addiction to anything, if the means to their *drug* is available immediately—with powerful societal pressure to take it—it's going to be very hard to resist and abstain. This is what people with restrictive eating disorders are up against. If eating disorders are on the rise today in both young people and in older adults, it's easy to understand why.

---

1. Watson, HJ, Yilmaz, Z, Thornton, LM et al. Genome-wide association study identifies eight risk loci and implicates metabo-psychiatric origins for anorexia nervosa. Nat Genet 51, 1207-1214 (2019). https://doi.org/10.1038/s41588-019-04 39-2.

2. Scharner S, Stengel A. Animal models for anorexia nervosa: A systematic review. Front Hum Neurosci. 2021 Jan 20; 14:596381. doi: 10.3389/fnhum.2020.596381. PMID: 33551774; PMCID: PMC7854692.

3. Madra M, Zeltser LM. BDNF-Val66Met variant and adolescent stress interact to promote susceptibility to anorexic behavior in mice. Transl Psychiatry. 2016 Apr 5; 6(4): e776. doi: 10.1038/tp.2016.35. PMID: 27045846; PMCID: PMC4872394.

4. BEAT Report. 'When Do Eating Disorders Start: An Investigation into Two Large UK Samples.' 2021: https://beat.contentfiles.net/media/documents/Age _of_ED_Onset_Report.pdf.

5. Mack, T., Sanchez-Roige, S. & Davis, L.K. Genetic investigation of the contribution of body composition to anorexia nervosa in an electronic health record setting. Transl Psychiatry 12, 486 (2022). https://doi.org/10.1038/s41398-022-02251-y.

6. Huckins LM, Signer R, Johnson J, Wu YK, Mitchell KS, Bulik CM. What next for eating disorder genetics? Replacing myths with facts to sharpen our understanding. Mol Psychiatry. 2022 Oct;27(10):3929-3938. doi: 10.1038/s41380-022-01601-y. Epub 2022 May 20. PMID: 35595976; PMCID: PMC9718676.

# Chapter Nine

# The Minnesota Starvation Experiment & Effects of Starvation

W hen you have a restrictive eating disorder, your body is in a state of energy deficit, which in simpler terms is a state of semi-starvation. This is true whether you look *starved* in a skin-and-bone emaciated sense or not. If your body weight is below the level that your brain recognises to be optimal for your health, then you are in a state of starvation.

A starved state will occur when you are consistently eating restrictively and/or compensating for the energy you do take in. This doesn't only relate to people eating a few hundred calories a day or running a hundred miles a week. You can be eating amounts that might on the surface seem *enough* or *adequate*, but if it's below the requirements of your body, then you will be in a semi-starved state. In addition to this, while your body stores of fat and lean tissues remain below the level that is optimal for your set point, you will also stay in a state of semi-starvation. And because you are in a semi-starved state with a restrictive eating disorder, it's important to know about the Minnesota Starvation Experiment and the effects that semi-starvation can have on you.

• • • ● • ● • • •

# The Minnesota Starvation Experiment

Even though it's now nearly eighty years since it was conducted, the Minnesota Starvation Experiment[1] remains our best source of data about what happens when someone is food deprived or semi-starved. It still informs doctors and scientists today who aim to help people who have become starved or experienced significant weight loss for any reason, including famines, cancers and eating disorders.

The experiment was conducted during the Second World War between 1944-1945. The intention was to study the effects of dietary restriction and develop an understanding of how best to support people as they overcome a starved state. This information was sought to improve understanding of how best to rehabilitate people during the post-war period who had been food deprived or prisoners of war.

The experiment was conducted by Dr Ancel Keys and Dr Josef Brozeck. They recruited thirty-six healthy young men, ranging in age between twenty and thirty-three, who were conscientious objectors to the war. The men were tested for their physical and mental health and were selected from over two hundred volunteers.

The initial experiment was made up of three phases:

## The Three-Month Control Period

During this initial phase, the men were fed individualised amounts that ensured they maintained their ideal body weight (also called their control weight). The average amount that each man was fed in this period was 3,492 calories.

## The Six-Month Semi-Starvation Phase

This phase was designed to ensure that each man lost 25 percent of his ideal body weight. The average intake during this period was 1,570 calories. This amount was higher or lower depending on the rate of individual weight loss. The men's intake was provided in two meals a day and made up of mainly cabbage, potatoes and dark bread in order to mimic typical European wartime diets.

## The Three-Month Rehabilitation Phase

From the initial thirty-six men who entered the experiment, thirty-two reached this phase. They were divided into four groups, and each group was fed a different controlled amount—either an additional 400, 800, 1,200 or 1,600 calories to the amount they had been fed in the semi-starvation phase. After five weeks of refeeding at this level, the rate of improvement was much slower than expected, and so the intake of the men was reviewed again. This is discussed in more detail below.

## The Unrestricted Rehabilitation Phase

After the experiment, twelve men volunteered to remain on for another two months to be monitored.

The idea of this phase was to allow the men to eat with no restrictions for a further eight weeks of observation. What and how much they ate was still closely monitored.

## Findings from the Control Period

In this initial phase of the study, when each man was eating enough to maintain his ideal body weight, the men were said to feel good; they were energised and engaged. They volunteered in local community projects, some studied at the university, and they took part in a variety of cultural activities in the city. They were essentially fit and healthy young men who were interested in life, engaged, social and active.

## Findings from the Semi-Starvation Phase

As the men entered the semi-starvation phase, at which point their calories were cut by around half the number they had needed to maintain their control weight, they generally remained in good spirits for the first few weeks and interested in their weight loss. However, as time went on several significant physical, psychological, social and cognitive symptoms developed.

Physically, they became increasingly weak. In 2002, nineteen of the original men who took part in the study were interviewed about their experiences by researchers[2]. One of the men could remember not being able to open a department store door because he had become so weak. They developed a decreased tolerance of the cold, dizziness, vertigo, tiredness, hair loss, reduced coordination and ringing to their ears. The men had a dramatic drop in their heart rate and blood pressure. Some of the men developed significant oedema. Their need to urinate increased and their digestive system slowed down, giving them constipation and other stomach issues. Cuts and bruises healed more slowly, and sleep became interrupted. Their sex drive and interest in relationships also disappeared.

Mentally, the men became increasingly irritable and impatient. Little things their friends did that would usually not bother them now made them very upset. They became annoyed by the eating habits of other people. Over the three months, the men became increasingly withdrawn and introverted. The researchers observed indifference and boredom among them. Some pulled out of their university classes because they no longer had the motivation or mental energy to attend. Depression was also observed. They started to neglect their personal hygiene, had difficulty making decisions, lost their sense of humour and developed more rigid thinking. They increasingly found conversation with others difficult and pointless, and if they did go to the cinema, they found they could recognise comedy but no longer felt compelled to laugh.

Food obsession also developed. Eating in ritualised ways became standard. Some of the men would eat very slowly to make the food last longer, while others would eat incredibly quickly. Licking of plates at the end of a meal became the norm. The men became upset at the sight of food waste, and many reported dreaming about food. Some of the men would go to diners just to watch other people eating, while others would actively avoid having to see others eat when they couldn't. Some of the men collected cookbooks, with one participant later reporting that during the study period, he collected over a hundred. Food became their main focus, with one man later reporting that food became the most important, if not the only, thing in life, reflecting that this also makes life *pretty dull.*

During the start of the semi-starvation phase, the men were still allowed to freely drink water and tea and coffee. This resulted in many of them being observed to drink coffee and tea obsessively to fill their stomach. It was soon decided by Keys that this consumption needed to be limited, and so the men were then restricted to nine cups a day. They were also allowed to chew gum during this stage of the experiment, but this also dramatically increased, to the point one man (later removed from the experiment) was observed to chew up to forty packs a day.

The men reported trying to keep themselves distracted from their hunger as best they could. Some of them started to collect and hoard both food and non-food-related items that they didn't need, such as books or trinkets. In the 2002 interviews, one of the men still couldn't make sense of the hoarding behaviour he experienced at the time.

For some of the men, their behaviour and psychological state became more concerning. One man was chopping wood one day with an axe and cut off three of his fingers. Years later when interviewed, he said, *I admit to being crazy mixed up at the time. I am not ready to say that I did it on purpose. I am not ready to say that I didn't.* Keys rushed to see him when he was in hospital after the incident, and the man begged Keys to allow him to stay in the experiment, which Keys did reluctantly agree to. The man completed the study without any further issues.

Four men didn't complete the experiment. Of these, two were hospitalised during the semi-starvation phase for *pre-psychotic symptoms*. One man impulsively broke his diet repeatedly and began to go on minor shoplifting sprees, stealing sweets and trinkets that were all but worthless to him. He was seen to write voluminously and creatively. He was admitted to a psychiatric ward after he developed a violent emotional outburst and threatened suicide. After being allowed to eat freely again, his mental state and behaviours quickly returned to normal.

Another man stole some food items and rooted in rubbish bins. He was dropped from the experiment due to failure to lose weight. At this point, he ate huge amounts in a binge-like way, causing him to vomit, and he sought admission for psychiatric help. His symptoms also subsided after a few weeks, and he later denied experiencing any further psychiatric problems during his lifetime.

Of the final two participants not to remain to the end, one had an episode of passing blood in his urine and was taken out of the experiment. It's reported that soon after he was eating normally again, his urine cleared. The final participant didn't lose weight at the rate Keys hoped, and so Keys suspected him of cheating. The man denied it, but Keys omitted his data from the results that were published.

### Findings from the Rehabilitation Phase

For some of the men in the starvation experiment, the start of the rehabilitation phase was the most challenging part. One man later stated that this period was no better than the semi-starvation phase in a large part because there was no noticeable relief from feelings of hunger, despite now being given more food.

Many of the men were surprised when they initially lost weight in this refeeding stage. This was attributed to their loss of oedema as they ate a bit more. The men were also frustrated that they were still extremely weak, and this took longer to improve than they hoped.

During the beginning of the twelve-week rehabilitation phase, the men were split into four groups, each group receiving a different increased number of calories to the level they were receiving during the semi-starvation phase. The men didn't know which group they were in, and none of them believed themselves to be in the group receiving the highest amounts. The lowest group at this time were receiving just an additional 400 calories a day to the amount they had been eating. After five weeks, the rate of improvements in the men was much slower than Keys was expecting, although this was proportional to which group they were in. At this point, Keys and the research team increased the feeding amounts again by another 800 calories a day, so they were either given an additional 1,200, 1,600, 2,000 or 2,400 a day to their starvation level. This did result in some more noticeable rises in weight, and more importantly the mood of the men improved. Levels of depression were noted to reduce in line with how much food the man was now receiving.

After three months of controlled refeeding, none of the men were back at their starting weight. On average, weights were back to 36.7 percent of what they had lost. Physically, the men still felt a long way from their pre-starvation levels of energy and strength. When interviewed later, all the men agreed that they were not back to normal after the three-month rehabilitation period.

**Findings from the Unrestricted Rehabilitation Phase**

At this point of the experiment, twelve men stayed on to be observed and monitored over another eight weeks during which they could eat unrestrictedly.

The men described feeling a complete loss of control over their eating when they could eat freely, and many ate abundantly. One of the men in the later interviews described a day when he had eaten several large meals in town in a very short space of time and was sick on the bus on the way back to the accommodation because his stomach couldn't cope with it. He said that he simply couldn't satisfy his craving for food despite a full stomach.

Another man during this time had to be taken to hospital to have his stomach pumped as he had eaten so much.

Over half the men when allowed to eat freely again described overeating because of this urge to keep eating despite feeling full. A third of the men reported binge eating, described as eating excessively with a feeling of loss of control over their actions.

In the first couple of weeks of the unrestricted rehabilitation phase, most of the men ate high amounts with some eating up to 11,500 calories a day.

When Keys and the researchers observed these what they considered overeating behaviours, they became concerned and reintroduced some control over food access in the week but not at weekends. In doing so they noted a pattern of *weekend gorging* in the men. The men were observed to eat 50–200 percent more food at the weekends than during the days of controlled refeeding in the week.

## Longer-Term Findings of the Experiment

Taking part in the Minnesota Starvation Study had an impact on the men for much longer than the study ran.

In the later interviews of nineteen of the men when they were in their eighties, ten reported that their food perceptions and perspectives were forever altered by the experiment.

One man described the year following the experiment as a *year-long cavity* that needed to be filled and a year of eating *excessively*. In fact, when reviewed eight months after the rehabilitation phase, around a third of the men still reported eating large quantities of food.

Some of the men reported that it was at least two years before they felt that their body had fully recovered, with a return to their previous strength and stamina.

When it came to their weight, after eight months of rehabilitation, their weight was seen to have peaked, with some men entering the *overweight* range (by BMI) but none into the *obese*. Body fat percentage rose above their control period values in the weeks and months after the experiment. This is a phenomenon that we now understand to be *fat overshoot*, and it's discussed in more detail in Chapter 10.

When the men were asked about their weight gain in the rehabilitation phase, seven of the men reported that they had been concerned about the initial fat accumulation on their abdomen and buttocks, and that this had made them feel *fat*. They could remember that as they gained weight, it was initially distributed in different places to where they had carried weight before, as they felt their thighs, buttocks and midsection all appeared fuller and their face fatter.

Most of the men reported that it took around two years for their body weight to stabilise back to their control period weight range and distribution.

The depression seen in all the men improved rapidly when they were eating freely again. One man who reported a *deep, dark depression* during the experiment reported it improved during the rehabilitation phase, and he experienced no further psychiatric problems in his lifetime.

The adult children of one of the men were interviewed recently[3], and they reported that their father's relationship with food and his body was forever altered by the experiences he went through in the experiment. They could recall him telling them that food deprivation was the hardest thing that could ever be inflicted on a person, leaving them feeling a loss of any kind of life sustenance. They also spoke about the fact that their father was always hungry and always had to have food close at hand, so he knew it was there when he needed it.

After the study, many of the men went into either charitable work that involved getting food to the starving or hungry, and a couple of them even had careers working with people who were deprived or hungry. There was a sense of need to support others who were starved because of their understanding and empathy for how hard hunger is.

Despite all that the men went through over their months in the starvation experiment, all but one of them said that if asked they would repeat it.

· · · ● ● · ● ● · ·

# Relating the Minnesota Starvation Experiment to Restrictive Eating Disorders

The Minnesota Starvation Experiment is an experiment that today would never stand up to ethical approval and so could never be repeated. It therefore remains the best data available to teach us about the full effects of starvation, the process of refeeding and emerging from a semi-starved state. The details in the experiment give a clear indication of what physical symptoms, behaviours, social and psychological signs and weight changes are common to anyone in a semi-starved state and what to expect once free eating resumes.

This information has also been critical in informing us about some of the commonly seen signs and symptoms in restrictive eating disorders. It helps us to identify which symptoms people commonly experience might be purely related to the body being in a semi-starved state and what's related to the eating disorder itself. The experiment also gives us information about what's to be expected in the process of overcoming a restrictive eating disorder in relation to eating more and gaining weight, including potential time frames for physical restoration.

For anyone reading this who has a restrictive eating disorder, perhaps a key point to note is that these men in this experiment were *semi-starved* for six months. In just six months, these men experienced all the difficulties from the physical, psychological, behavioural, social and emotional perspectives described above. Compare this to someone with an eating disorder who has usually been restricting their intake and living in a semi-starved state for much longer. However, just as these men reported a return to full health and normal lives after their return to free eating, so, too, do people who have had restrictive eating disorders for any length of time.

One of the key study findings in relation to the effect starvation had on these men that does differ significantly to people with eating disorders relates to physical energy levels. The study findings reported that the men all became very lethargic, lost their strength and became slower in their movements. None of the men were reported to experience hyperactivity as part of the starvation effects. In people with restrictive eating disorders, however, hyperactivity is a key feature, where many people with eating disorders actually feel more energised and hyperactive when they are in a state of energy deficit. This indicates that the hyperactivity and false sense of energy seen in people with restrictive eating disorders is a definite symptom of the eating disorder and not a normal response to hunger or starvation. This is where the evolutionary and genetic theories for eating disorders are beneficial as they help to explain this anomaly.

The Minnesota Study results clearly demonstrated that semi-starvation can result in binge eating (in which the men reported a loss of control over what or how much they ate). This has also been seen and reported in prisoners of war upon having access to food again. Therefore, people with binge eating as part of their restrictive eating disorder are experiencing a very normal physiological reaction of the body to hunger and starvation. None of these men had eating disorders and their binges stopped after a few weeks or months of being able to eat freely again.

Even of those men who didn't experience loss of control binge eating, the majority still reported or were observed to eat high amounts when they could after the semi-starvation period. In the first weeks, intake was estimated for some to be around 11,000 calories a day, and some of the men were still eating high amounts eight months after the study. One man reported that it took three years for his hunger and eating patterns to return to what he considered a more *normal* level. Once again, remember that these men were only semi-starved for six months for it to have had this impact.

The next point worth highlighting relates to physical healing and weight gain. The men reported that on average they felt that it took around two years for them to feel physically back to where they had been when they entered the experiment. This demonstrates that even with good food intake over a lengthy time, the body takes time to fully repair and heal from any period of semi-starvation.

With weight gain, the men all gained an excess of fat in the initial weight restoration phase to their fat levels before the experiment. They initially regained on average 10–14 percent more weight than they were at their control weight range, which we can consider their genetic set point weight. Many of the men expressed concern at the gains of fat around their midsection, thighs and buttocks. This is a clear demonstration of what we today consider the overshoot phenomenon. The body needs to regain more fat stores initially in order to carry out the full non-fat mass tissue restoration and repairs that are needed. When this has been done, any ongoing excess weight is naturally lost (see Chapter 10).

Today we know that people can be semi-starved and mal-nourished at any weight or shape if they have lost weight below their genetic set weight range. Those who have restrictive eating disorders but are not at the low end of the BMI spectrum might be wondering why the men in this study all reached a weight that would be considered *underweight* by BMI charts. This can be explained because all the men selected for the study were of genetically small builds. The average BMI of the men before the study started was 21.9, which even for young, muscular men is low. Even the man with the highest genetic weight at the start only had a BMI of 25.4. They each lost on average just under 25 percent of their start weight during the experiment, which meant their weight dropped to that lower end of the BMI spectrum. However, the effects of semi-starvation on a person are the same whether you are at a low BMI range or you are still in the normal range after weight loss. Therefore, the information from this study applies equally to those with restrictive eating disorders in bigger bodies as it does in smaller ones.

To highlight this point further, the men in the study who did have slightly higher natural set weights also remained at higher weights as they lost weight. This upset Keys, who was concerned they were not losing enough weight, and they had the most significant cuts in their intake of all the men. The symptoms these men in the higher weight range experienced from semi-starvation were exactly the same as those in the lower range.

Of course, the men in the Minnesota Starvation Study didn't have restrictive eating disorders. They didn't have an addiction to the energy deficit that the semi-starvation caused. For them, a state of negative energy was intensely uncomfortable from the beginning, and they were desperate to eat again and return their body to a state of energy balance. This is significantly different to a person with an eating disorder who has positive reinforcement coming from their addicted brain because of the energy deficit created by their semi-starved situation.

By the time a person with an eating disorder seeks support or wants to change and overcome it, they have also usually had the eating disorder with the associated restrictive eating and behaviours for longer than six months. Therefore, the brain circuitry that drives these habits and behaviours has had a significant amount of time to become strongly learnt and reinforced.

The final noteworthy point from the study is that the men reported that the most challenging time for them was during the initial rehabilitation phase, when their calories were increased but still restricted. The men reported that this was a distressing time because they had such a deep hunger that was still not satiated despite more food. There is a perhaps stark comparison here to the use of meal plans for people overcoming eating disorders. When using a meal plan during the process of overcoming an eating disorder, it's hard to ensure that the food amounts given on the plan will meet the deep hunger present. For people on a plan who are not getting enough food, just like the men in this study, it can be a very distressing experience. Meal plans need to be used with care to ensure that they are never restrictive to someone who is experiencing confusing and challenging deep levels of hunger while in the process of emerging from a semi-starved state.

In the next section, starvation syndrome is discussed in more detail, using the teachings of the Minnesota study to inform our understanding of it and relating it to restrictive eating disorders.

Overall, the Minnesota Starvation Study is incredibly important, and understanding its findings should help you understand some of the symptoms you experience that can be related to being in a semi-starved state. The findings should also reassure you that high hunger, eating beyond physical fullness, binges and potentially gaining more weight in the restoration process than your genetic set weight range is all absolutely normal.

• • • •• • • • •• •

# Starvation Syndrome

When you understand a restrictive eating disorder as your brain being addicted to the state of energy deficit, you can recognise that any energy-deficit-creating behaviours will result in a high reward response and in themselves become addictive. This will help you to appreciate why behaviours such as restrictive eating and compensatory methods are as alluring and difficult to stop as they are.

However, there are other symptoms and behaviours commonly seen in people with restrictive eating disorders that don't in themselves create energy deficit. These arise instead because of your body being in a state of energy deficit, which is also referred to as semi-starvation.

During a restrictive eating disorder, your body becomes under-fuelled and undernourished, effectively entering a semi-starved state. You might not believe this is the case for you because you think someone who is starving must look emaciated, perhaps imagining a stereotypical person with anorexia or starved people in third world countries. If your body isn't as visually starved as this, it's likely that you falsely believe that you can't be affected by malnourishment and starvation. Another common misconception is that to be starved, you must be living on a diet that's barely more than an apple or salad a day. As your restrictive diet is probably more than this, you will also believe it impossible that you are in a state of starvation.

At the end of the day, if you have a restrictive eating disorder, you are addicted to energy deficit. A body that's in a state of energy deficit is not at the genetic weight it should be to function optimally, no matter what your body shape, weight or size. As a result of being in a state of energy deficit, your body and brain will be affected by something called *starvation syndrome*.

Starvation syndrome (or semi-starvation) affects anyone who is in an ongoing state of energy deficit and below their genetic body weight and size. It describes the physical and psychological changes due to prolonged energy restriction—through an eating disorder or any other factors that lead someone to take in less energy than they are using. Other common examples are from ordinary dieting or other illnesses, such as some gastrointestinal conditions or cancers.

The Minnesota Starvation Experiment is the best experimental evidence there is of the physical, psychological, cognitive and social consequences of semi-starvation. The experiment was discussed in detail in the last section.

The symptoms observed in the men who were semi-starved for six months during the Minnesota Starvation Experiment have since been reported in similar studies on prisoners of war or those who have faced starvation from famine situations. This has led medical experts to understand the typical signs and symptoms of *starvation syndrome*, which are listed below.

**Physical Symptoms**

- Heart muscle mass can shrink. In the Minnesota Experiment, heart mass was observed to reduce by an average of 25 percent.

- The body metabolism slows down. In the Minnesota Experiment, a 40 percent average reduction in metabolism was observed.

- Hormonal changes may result in low or no sex drive. Women may experience changes to their menstrual cycle, and men can experience difficulties with erections and sperm motility.

- Other symptoms include:

- A reduction in heart rate and blood pressure;

- Dizziness, vertigo and blackouts;

- Oedema;

- Loss of strength and extreme tiredness;

- Muscle cramps;

- Nerve tingling;

- Feeling cold all the time;

- Dry and brittle hair, as well as hair loss;

- Dry skin and weak nails;

- Frequent urination;

- Lanugo—a fine hair that grows on the body; and

- Slow gut motility and constipation or other digestive symptoms.

**Emotional Changes**

- Depression

- Anxiety

- Irritability

- Lack of motivation

- Social withdrawal

- Loss of ambition and interest in life

- Increased noise sensitivity

- Feeling frustrated with oneself

- Sudden bursts of anger

**Cognitive Changes (changes to thinking)**

- Impaired concentration, judgment and decision-making

- Increased rigid thinking

- Increase in obsessional thoughts

- Reduced alertness

- Impaired comprehension

## Social Changes

- Withdrawal and isolation

- Strained relationships

- Less interest in appearance or personal hygiene

- Loss of a sense of humour and the ability to laugh

- Feelings of social inadequacy

## Behaviours Related to Food and Eating

- Food obsession; thinking about food all the time

- Meticulous meal planning

- Focus only on mealtimes

- Eating very fast or very slowly

- Playing with food or creating strange food combinations

- Acceptance of boring or tasteless food

- Binge eating episodes—eating large amounts in a short space of time with an associated sense of loss of control

- Hoarding behaviours, e.g., collecting recipes, food or food-related items, such as cups, spoons, containers, etc.

- Anger if food is seen to be wasted

- Increased fluid consumption, particularly coffee, and excessive gum chewing

- Using more condiments, spices and salt for flavour

If you recognise any of these symptoms in yourself, then it's very likely you are affected by starvation syndrome. Some of these typical behaviours that initially arose from starvation syndrome will have formed part of the rituals and addictive behaviours that your brain found reward in and so latched on to. When overcoming an eating disorder, it can be difficult to know initially which of these behaviours will improve spontaneously through re-nourishment alone and which will require more re-programming efforts to overcome. Therefore, re-nourishment and physical healing are always key priorities.

Again, *you can have starvation syndrome at any weight or size.* You don't need to be underweight by BMI charts to have a severe and medically dangerous restrictive eating disorder or malnourished body. Starvation syndrome will affect anyone who is not taking in enough energy to meet their body's needs.

For someone who has starvation syndrome because of something other than an eating disorder, there will be a drive to eat to restore their energy balance as soon as it becomes possible for them to do so. When you have an eating disorder with a powerful addiction to the state of energy deficit, overcoming it is not as simple.

If you have a restrictive eating disorder, you are likely to have had the behaviours that arose from starvation syndrome for a lot longer than six months. Therefore, some of these symptoms have become embedded into your brain and formed into behavioural habits or habits of thought or emotion. This takes more brain reprogramming to overcome than getting out of energy deficit alone. Of course, this is not impossible. It just requires a focus on changing all these behaviours and thought patterns as you work through the process to overcome the eating disorder.

---

1. Leah M. Kalm, Richard D. Semba. They starved so that others be better fed: Remembering Ancel Keys and the Minnesota Experiment. The Journal of Nutrition, Volume 135, Issue 6, June 2005, Pages 1347-1352, https://doi.org/10.109 3/jn/135.6.1347.

2. Eckert, Elke & Gottesman, Irving & Swigart, Susan & Casper, Regina. (2018). A 57-YEAR FOLLOW-UP INVESTIGATION AND REVIEW OF THE MINNESOTA STUDY ON HUMAN STARVATION AND ITS RELEVANCE TO EATING DISORDERS. 2.

3. Malcolm Gladwell, Revisionist History Podcast.

# Chapter Ten

---

# All About Weight & Hunger

## Set Point Theory Is Not Just About Weight

### What Is Set Point Theory and How Does It Relate to Weight, Fat Stores & Energy Expenditure?

Your brain and body love homeostasis. They want to keep everything at a stable level and to protect these levels. When your brain has a baseline (or homeostatic) level for something it recognises as being optimal for function, it can quickly notice when there has been a change that needs to be addressed.

A key example of this relates to body temperature. Your body has a temperature range of around 36-37 degrees (when you're healthy) at which it functions optimally. If you go under or above that range, then your brain will quickly take action to try to bring your temperature back to the acceptable level. It may, for example, create thoughts telling you to put on or remove clothing or by promoting shivering or sweating.

As discussed in Chapter 3 regarding the dopamine model of addiction, your brain likes to maintain a baseline level of dopamine. When dopamine levels go above or below this level, your brain will take action to attempt to correct it.

This same principle applies to other chemicals and processes within your body. Energy expenditure, weight, and fat supplies are three other factors for which each of us has a largely genetically determined homeostatic level (or set point range) which our brains will attempt to protect and maintain.

It's thought that epigenetics, in addition to full genetics and environmental factors, is a key contributor to determining your set point. *Epigenetics* is the term used to describe the way in which your environment, or even the behaviours or experiences of your parents or grandparents, can impact how your genes are expressed. These factors do not change the DNA code, but they do change how your body interprets the code.

Set point weight theory has been around since the early 1980s, when two researchers proposed that everybody has a pre-programmed set point weight at which it's most comfortable and able to function optimally. According to set point weight theory, your brain will attempt to adjust food intake and/or energy expenditure to correct any mismatch between your body's current weight and set point weight.

There is natural speculation around this theory and ongoing research. However, the fact that the average adult human will predominantly stay around the same weight range (give or take a few kilograms) throughout their adult life suggests there are strong mechanisms at play to protect that range. Examples of this are frequently seen when people (without eating disorders) attempt to diet and successfully lose some weight. It is known that over 80 percent will regain that weight in the mid to longer term[1], returning to a very similar weight to that at which they started. Similarly, where experiments have been done to attempt to push people to a higher weight, for example by enticing them to gain weight through monetary rewards, very few can sustain it for long before their body seems to take over and drive their weight back to their previous level.

In recent years, scientists who research set point weight theory have come to the understanding that body weight regulation is very likely controlled by the body's fat store levels and not overall weight[2]. The hormone leptin, which is produced in fat tissues, is the key player in this. Leptin is discussed in more detail later in this chapter.

In the case of the men who took part in the Minnesota Starvation Experiment, the extreme levels of eating they were observed to engage in after the semi-starvation period ended were proportional to their levels of fat store depletion. This extreme hunger improved relative to their restoration of not just weight but body fat. It's therefore thought that the drive to eat excessively in a person who is below their natural weight is part of the body's regulatory system to restore weight and an optimal level of fat mass. It's worth repeating here that this level is unique for everyone.

If you have low fat stores and therefore low levels of leptin, a warning is sent to the hypothalamus in your brain that fat supplies are below your body's set point and that there is food deprivation. This tells your brain it needs to switch on biological mechanisms to drive energy intake and so create strong urges to eat. At the same time, your hypothalamus will lower your metabolism to reduce the amount of energy being used in a bid to restore fat supplies, because fat is your body's essential source of stored energy.

As stated above, one of the ways in which your brain attempts to reduce energy expenditure when you have low fat stores is by affecting your metabolism. When you are underfed relative to your energy needs and you lose weight, entering an energy deficit, your body will try to compensate by decreasing your total energy expenditure, resting energy expenditure and the energy used in the process of digesting and absorbing the foods that are eaten. If you are not eating enough, your body will lower your metabolism to save all the energy it can. On the flip side, if you *overeat* and gain weight, you will experience increases in your metabolism as your body attempts to burn off the excess calories consumed. These metabolic adaptations occur due to changes in the activity of your nervous system, thyroid hormones and leptin. This is your body's attempt to resolve any energy imbalance, preserve sufficient energy stores as fat and maintain a stable body weight longer term (at the set point level determined by your genetic and epigenetic factors).

When it comes to energy regulation, some in the science community now believe that the brain is in fact trying to maintain a set point level of energy balance and that set points of body weight and fat supplies are maintained because of this.

This theory stems from the understanding that the brain requires a high level of energy to keep functioning, and it will continue to protect this energy use as a priority, even when the body is energy deficient. In energy-balanced people, the brain's energy use is around 20 percent of their resting energy expenditure (how much energy that person uses at rest in twenty-four hours). In people who are below their natural weight, the relative proportion of the body's energy used by the brain rises to around 23 percent. This shows that when there is an energy shortage, there is a brain pull of energy from the extremities of the body to the brain. It's therefore hypothesised that the brain needs a constant energy budget, and so it wants to keep the whole body's energy in a tightly controlled range to protect its own energy supplies.

### Applying Set Point Theory to Overcoming a Restrictive Eating Disorder

This section has been quite scientific, but the take-home messages for you, if you are attempting to overcome a restrictive eating disorder, are:

- Everyone has a *set point* when it comes to levels of weight, fat stores and their body's energy balance, and your brain will do all it can to protect and maintain it.

- Your *set point* is largely determined by your genetics, external factors that have impacted how your genes are expressed and to a lesser extent your environment. This means your set point is unique to you and not something you can easily change.

- You might not like what your unique set point is in relation to weight or fat stores. It might be higher than society or health professionals tell you is *healthy*. However, continuing to hold your weight, fat stores and energy balance below your set point is only possible with ongoing restrictive eating and/or compensatory behaviours, which means holding on to the eating disorder and remaining miserable. If your set point is in the higher range and you have a naturally bigger body, you need to embrace it as a fabulous thing because that's where your physical and mental health and freedom ultimately lie.

- Set point theory is not just about weight. It's now understood to be related to the amount of fat stores you have. Fat stores produce a hormone called leptin, which sends signals to your brain related to energy availability. If leptin levels are low, your brain identifies this as insufficient fat stores and insufficient energy supplies. While this is the case, your brain will recognise that your body is in a state of energy deficit and do what it can to correct this.

- When your body is in a state of energy deficit, your brain will switch on processes to drive higher hunger and turn down your metabolism so that your body is using less energy for daily living. Metabolism is covered in more detail later in this chapter.

- If you enter a state of energy surplus, your brain will switch on processes to reduce energy intake and speed up your metabolism in an attempt to burn off the excess energy stores and restore energy balance. This means that if you gain weight as fat stores above your set point, your brain will use processes to attempt to bring it back to your level range.

- If you are aiming to overcome a restrictive eating disorder, all the above means that some weight gain is not enough. Restoration from a state of energy deficit is not just about restoring weight. It's also about restoring enough fat supplies. Until you restore your body in full, allowing yourself to gain weight both in terms of fat mass and fat-free mass, your body will not come out of energy deficit, and the addiction your brain has to energy deficit can never be overcome.

- Attempting to gain weight as muscle and not fat (how many times have I heard that?!?) will only prolong the process of physical healing and emerging from energy deficit. Your body needs the fat stores for energy balance, and until it gets them, no amount of muscle gain will allow you to fully overcome the current energy deficit state you are addicted to.

- Fears may arise of *gaining weight forever,* but according to set point theory, once your body has gained sufficient fat mass and fat-free mass for your unique set point, your brain will work hard to protect that level so that you don't gain above it forever more.

- For someone with a restrictive eating disorder and addiction to energy deficit, it's incredibly hard to override the rewarding and calming behaviours that increase or maintain the state of energy deficit. However, the biological processes that your brain will use to restore energy balance are not broken if you trust them. So, it's likely that as you abstain from restriction and resist engaging in compensatory behaviours, the same symptoms that someone without an eating disorder will experience will emerge. These include high hunger to push you to eat more, and fatigue to save all the energy possible as your brain does all it can to restore you to an energy-balanced state.

- To remain free of the eating disorder in future, you must stay out of energy deficit. This means doing everything you can to prevent your body fat levels from falling below your set point range throughout your future life.

· · ● ●· ● · ● ● · ·

# Fat Overshoot or Collateral Fattening

Now that you have more understanding of set point theory in relation to weight, fat levels and energy balance in your body, you also need to know a little more about the concept of fat overshoot.

Fat overshoot is commonly seen in people who are overcoming a state of semi-starvation as their body restores weight and fully repairs all tissues, organs and structures. In the last section I explained that you have a largely genetically determined set point for your weight and level of fat stores. If you attempt to sustain a weight or fat mass level below this point, your body will remain in a state of energy deficit and suboptimal mental and physical health. The concept I didn't cover in the previous section was that to reach your set point level of fat mass, you are likely going to need to first *overshoot* it.

Fat overshoot is necessary for your body to fully restore all the lean tissues that were lost during a period of starvation. Once your body has fully restored both fat mass and lean tissue, the *overshoot* fat mass will gradually be lost, bringing the level back to your set point. This eventual loss of the fat overshoot weight is a natural process. No dieting or attempts to *lose the overshoot* should be undertaken or it will simply take you back to a semi-starved state and into the alluring and addictive arms of the eating disorder.

Much of the knowledge we have about the fat overshoot phenomenon in people emerging from a state of energy deficit or semi-starvation comes from the data gained during the Minnesota Starvation Experiment (see Chapter 9).

The young men in the experiment lost on average 25 percent of their total body weight. As they went through the rehabilitation stage, fat overshoot was observed. After approximately twenty weeks of increased food intake, with many entering periods of *hyperphagia* (excessive eating), the men began to regain more body weight and fat stores than they had lost. It was also noted that the urges to eat large amounts observed in these men continued until not just their fat mass stores were restored but until their lean tissue (or fat-free mass) stores were also back at their previous baseline levels.

Therefore, the drive to *overeat* when overcoming a period of prolonged energy deficit is believed to come from a deficit in the body's fat mass as well as a deficit in the body's expected lean tissues. As lean tissues can only be fully restored after there is sufficient storage of fat, the process of restoring all lean tissue by *overeating* is only possible with associated excess stores of body fat, hence the fat overshoot.

When you are restoring your weight from a state of energy deficit, excess fat stores are essential for your body to complete restoration of lean tissues. These include muscles, internal organs, skin, the nervous system and all other cells in the body. Until both tissue types are restored, your body is not able to fully heal and repair, and you will remain in a state of energy deficit.

## Why Does Your Body Restore Fat Faster Than Lean Tissue, Leading to This Overshoot?

It isn't fully understood why your body needs to store excess fat mass to complete restoration of lean tissue in the process of overcoming a state of energy deficit. One thought is that it relates to energy conservation measures still being switched on that your body used when energy intake was low, causing this faster restoration in fat recovery to that of lean tissue. This theory relates to the idea that your body remains in a state of survival response, an adaptive technique to ensure a faster return to being able to survive another period of food scarcity. Your body will only emerge from survival response mode when both fat mass and lean tissue stores are fully restored.

There are other credible explanations for why your body needs to go through this fat overshoot process:

- Lean tissue has a capacity for how quickly it can be built and deposited in your body, whereas fat can be deposited much faster. Therefore, there is a temporary de-synchronisation between the restoration of fat mass to lean tissue, which results in fat overshoot.

- Hyperphagia (or the drive to eat a lot) is driven in part by inadequate lean tissue stores, not just by insufficient fat mass. Therefore, the extreme hunger many experience as they come out of a semi-starved state continues until both lean mass and fat mass are fully restored, causing this accumulation of excess fat.

Science experts agree that because of the way fat is gained faster than lean tissue, in someone regaining weight from a state of being underweight (meaning under their set point weight and fat level), fat overshoot is a prerequisite to the complete recovery of lean tissue and full internal repairs. In this way the body laying down this overshoot fat is a form of collateral to the body's full restoration; a concept researchers refer to as *collateral fattening*[3]!

## How Much Weight and How Long Will It Last?

This is one of those million–dollar questions that everyone wants an answer to as they go through the already mentally and emotionally challenging process of overcoming an eating disorder. It might feel cruel that you not only have to gain weight in a society where weight gain is too often deemed *unhealthy* or goes against cultural beauty standards, but you also have to exceed your natural set point for fat stores as you fully physically restore.

It would be amazing if I could say that this is how much you will gain above your set point, and this is how long it will last. Of course, you already knew I couldn't do that.

Every human body is different. All kinds of other factors will impact your unique body needs and time taken to adjust. Consistency with eating enough and allowing the process to continue uninterrupted will of course be a key factor in ensuring that it's as smooth and efficient as possible.

Having said that, a very rough idea of how much weight is gained in an average, healthy person and how long it lasts can be found from the Minnesota Starvation Experiment data. This data has also since been verified by other smaller studies of people who have gained weight from a state of energy deficit.

The men in the Minnesota Starvation Experiment gained on average four kilograms of excess weight as fat overshoot to their pre-starvation levels. This ranged from zero to nine kilograms amongst the men studied. In terms of how long it took for their weight to settle, on average it took one to two years for the men to naturally feel that their body was back to their pre-starvation level and for their fat stores to return to where they had been. Of course, for some this time was less (six months to a year), while one man reported it took four to five years. To my understanding, though, one of the men did enter a state of weight cycling with a disrupted relationship with food after the experiment, and this will have impacted how quickly his body weight and fat levels settled back to their pre-experiment level.

It's important not to get hung up on these figures. They are included here to provide some reassurance that this process is not a quick fix. But over-comparison only leads to heightened anxiety, and every human body differs. When you consider the Minnesota Starvation Experiment men, it's also important to remember that they were not emerging from an addiction to the state of energy deficit. In their case, if there was an addiction to any kind of internal energy state, it would have been to energy surplus and ultimately restoring a state of energy equilibrium. This means their ability to work through the process of weight restoration and fat overshoot was less complicated than for someone with a restrictive eating disorder.

Another interesting finding in the research is that in the Minnesota Starvation Experiment and in more recent studies looking at people who diet and then regain an *overshoot* of fat, the people who gain the most overshoot are those whose natural set point is leaner than others. Therefore, if a person has a genetically naturally leaner body, it's possible they will experience a higher degree of overshoot in fat stores through the restoration process than people who have a genetically higher set point for body fat.

Finally, research has also demonstrated that what people eat when overcoming a state of semi-starvation and restoring weight makes no difference to how the weight is gained. Whether you eat protein, carbs or fats and how much of each of these macronutrients you have is of little significance to whether your body gains weight as fat or lean tissue. As Ancel Keys said over seventy years ago, *the most important thing to a weight restoration diet is abundant calories.* This statement has yet to be discredited.

## Applying the Concept of Fat Overshoot to Overcoming an Eating Disorder

What are the take-home messages about fat overshoot?

- Most importantly, don't try to avoid overshoot. The science shows that it's almost certainly a prerequisite to fully restore both fat and lean tissues. Until your body has restored both tissue types in full, you will remain in a state of energy deficit, meaning you won't be able to fully overcome the eating disorder.

- Use the concept of *collateral fattening* to remind yourself why extra gains in terms of fat stores are a necessary part of the physical restoration process. Gaining more fat than is needed later is your body laying down collateral to ensure the lean tissue can then be restored in full. If the fat collateral doesn't happen, neither does the final restoration of lean tissue.

- You don't overcome an addiction to energy deficit (i.e., a restrictive eating disorder) by staying in a state of energy deficit. The only way out of energy deficit is to go through the process of restoring both fat stores and lean tissue stores, allowing for fat overshoot. At this point, your brain will recognise that an energy-balanced state has been reached because your levels of fat mass and lean tissue are at your set point.

- It's impossible to say when your body has reached a point of *overshoot* or whether you are still earlier on in the process of gaining essential fat and lean tissue stores. High hunger levels will reduce when your body has restored all lean tissue as well as fat stores, and so a true reduction in hunger can be an indication that your body weight is at a point that it will naturally settle. However, avoid overanalysing your hunger. If you convince yourself it's dropping when it isn't, you risk going back to (unintentional) restriction.

- Focusing on and worrying about overshoot isn't letting go of the thoughts that are likely to trigger you back into automatically engaging in those addictive energy-deficit-creating behaviours. Therefore, try to refocus thoughts away from concerns about overshoot or fat levels and reframe them into positive thoughts about what a bigger body and mental freedom will bring you.

- Fully overcoming an eating disorder—gaining all the essential fat and lean tissue necessary and overcoming the mental addiction to energy deficit—is when you ultimately gain a future of endless opportunities and freedom. If you do end up with fat overshoot that's more than your set point and it does take a while to come down, it's surely still better than an addicted life with an eating disorder. Most people who get this far also report that when they reached *overshoot*, they stopped obsessing about their weight or size and felt genuine mental freedom and more happiness and body-confidence than they had in years. It takes trusting the process and allowing your body to keep gaining for as long as it needs to. In this way, you can see for yourself if fully emerging from energy deficit doesn't also help to change your own attitude to and confidence in your body.

- Finally, for anyone who has a susceptibility to a restrictive eating disorder, going back to a state of energy deficit is never an option to remain well. You don't have the luxury of having a body with lower fat stores than is healthy for you if you want to remain free of compulsive and addictive behaviours and hold on to mental freedom.

• • • • • • • • • •

# Extreme Hunger or Hyperphagia

### Feast Follows Famine

If you have read the previous sections on fat overshoot and set point theory, then you will have some understanding by now of why you can experience very high levels of hunger when you are overcoming a restrictive eating disorder. You should also be realising that this high level of hunger, if you allow it to, can drive you to eat what many consider to be *extreme* amounts of food. All of this explains why the concept of *extreme hunger* is so frequently referred to today in information and content related to eating disorders.

For anyone who is still unsure what's happening and why, or for those who need extra reassurance about extreme hunger, I will provide a short recap. Your body needs a given level of fat mass and lean tissue stores for your brain to recognise that your body is safely in a state of energy balance. The levels of fat and lean tissue that achieve this energy–balanced state are unique to you and largely determined by genetic factors. If your fat and lean tissue stores fall below your *set point,* your brain notices and recognises that you are in a state of energy deficit. Your brain then attempts to correct this by increasing fat and lean tissue stores back to the level it perceives is needed to function optimally.

To restore fat and lean tissue, your brain will switch off unnecessary functions to reduce your overall body metabolism and
minimise energy expenditure. It will also start to send high
hunger signals. This is when you develop *hyperphagia* or, as
people with eating disorders refer to it, *extreme hunger*.

Anyone who has undergone a period of semi-starvation,
which can arise from undereating and/or excessive energy expenditure and enters a state of energy deficit can experience
hyperphagia. This is your brain attempting to drive you back
to energy balance. It isn't just people with restrictive eating
disorders who experience this, but in today's culture it's most
widely recognised and understood in eating disorder communities. However, it was the Minnesota Starvation Study that
provided health professionals and scientists with the first (and
even now only) real data on the concept of hyperphagia in people
overcoming semi-starvation.

Looking then to the results from the Minnesota Starvation
Experiment, when allowed to eat freely again, around a third
of the men experienced binge eating—completely losing control
of their eating, and eating huge amounts. Over half of the men
otherwise reported extreme eating, in which they had a strong
urge to keep eating despite a stomach that was stretched to
capacity, but they maintained a sense of control over it.

In the first weeks of being allowed to eat freely after the end
of the main experiment, those men who were still having their
intake monitored were noted to eat up to 11,500 calories a day. In
follow-up studies, around a quarter of the men could remember

eating more or less continuously for a very long time after the experiment ended, suggesting that for some this hyperphagia lasted longer than some of the official figures suggest of between five and eight months.

The most notable finding from the Minnesota Experiment was that the men's excessive hunger came down in line with their body restoring first an overshoot level of fat mass and then full restoration of their lean tissue to their pre-starvation levels. Therefore, extreme hunger is understood to last for as long as it takes your body to fully restore fat mass and lean tissues to the level that is unique to your set point.

## What Does This Mean for You?

It's important to clarify—because many *experts* can still get this wrong—that having a restrictive eating disorder doesn't mean you have lost your natural hunger. It's true that your physical hunger might be blunted because it's been ignored for so long and so your brain stopped sending physical hunger signals in an attempt to preserve energy. But your body's biological and physiological hunger processes aren't broken. The fact is that you can be addicted to energy deficit with a restrictive eating disorder and still experience all the same symptoms of semi-starvation and the biological drive to eat. But the power of the addiction is so compelling that it will override those urges to eat. This was very likely once an evolutionary survival response, as was discussed in Chapter 7.

An addiction to energy deficit does not negate hunger symptoms. Your hunger will be present, and it will ignite even more as you abstain from restrictive eating.

If you are in the process of overcoming an eating disorder and experiencing extreme levels of hunger now, please be reassured that this is a very normal physiological response to semi-starvation. This is your body fighting for survival in the best way it knows how.

When you trust your hunger, it may well take your intake to very high levels, which could be above 10,000 calories, but this is normal and safe. It's not an indication that you have developed a food addiction or binge eating disorder.

This high level of hunger can last for several months or longer, depending on how much restoration work your body needs to do. That's not something you can control or should attempt to.

Once your body has restored full levels of fat mass (with very possible initial fat overshoot) and fully restored and repaired all your lean tissues and internal organs, your brain will recognise that your body is back in a state of energy balance. It will then turn down the extreme level of hunger you are experiencing.

Extreme hunger can be physically and mentally uncomfortable.

It's physically uncomfortable to eat so much food, especially when your stomach is not used to it, and to have an overly full stomach but to feel an ongoing high mental urge to keep eating. It's also mentally uncomfortable to experience this, and it can be distressing when you feel alone in the process if you have no contact with others who are going through it or have been through it.

The best thing you can do is trust the process, trust your body to know what it's doing, because it does. Its agenda is to get your health back to an optimal level, and it will do that if you respond to the signals it sends you. Flow with it and try to enjoy it where you can.

Remind yourself, you are not broken: your body is doing what any human body does when in a state of energy deficit. When that urge to eat everything and more hits, just tell yourself that feast always follows famine.

· · ● ● · ● ● · · ·

# Weight Gain as a Side Effect to Overcoming a Restrictive Eating Disorder

This chapter has focused a lot on weight, with information about set point theory and the concept of fat overshoot in relation to what can happen as anyone emerges from a period of energy deficit. This information is important to understand so that you are prepared for what will happen to your body as you go through the process of overcoming the eating disorder. It's helpful to know why these weight changes are so important to the process of full healing and that trying to interfere with them will jeopardise your body's ability to reach a state of energy balance.

The risk, though, of focusing too intensely on the weight changes that are a necessary part of the process to overcome an eating disorder is just that... It's given too much focus.

Focus on the weight gain takes attention away from the crucial part of not just overcoming an eating disorder but remaining free from it. This relates to the essential brain reprogramming work you need to do. Too much focus on your weight isn't going to be of benefit to you, and it can reinforce the stereotypical view that eating disorders are about weight alone.

One way in which it can help to view the weight gain is as a necessary side effect to the real work you are doing to overcome the addiction to energy deficit.

Weight gain is an essential part of overcoming a restrictive eating disorder. There's no avoiding that. You need to overcome the addiction to energy deficit by abstaining from behaviours that prolong a negative energy state and engage in behaviours that will create an energy surplus, to achieve a state of energy balance. This will naturally result in your body restoring much-needed fat stores and lean tissue stores and hence lead to weight gain. However, if weight gain and restoring energy balance were the only factors necessary to overcome an eating disorder, then treatment centres would have better success rates, or force-feeding people would work. Unfortunately, these measures don't work; overcoming an eating disorder requires much more.

The full process necessitates brain reprogramming by abstaining from the behaviours that drive the addiction to energy deficit. This involves unwiring old behaviours and wiring in new ones that ensure a return to and then maintenance of energy balance. The dopamine deficit that has built up over what is very likely years or decades of pursuing the eating disorder behaviours needs time to reset. The eating disorder has been a key coping mechanism for life stress and for emotional pain for a long time. Therefore, you need to develop and establish new coping mechanisms to ensure old eating disordered behaviours don't provide the automatic *fix* when life gets hard. New behaviours need to be embedded into circuitry that is adaptable to all kinds of environments and situations. This work takes time, hard work, challenging emotions and focused effort. Weight gain is a side effect to this process, but the true healing, life improvements and freedom gained as you overcome the eating disorder come from the mental and emotional work you do. This involves being self-empowered and making crucial life changes.

In the process of overcoming an eating disorder, weight gain is not something you need to overly focus on or attempt to manipulate. You are not as afraid of the weight gain as you believe yourself to be either (see Chapter 11). Yes, you will need to do some additional work around body acceptance and being able to see your weight gain in a positive light, but these form part of the mental and emotional changes that you go through in the process. Unfortunately, all too often family and friends or even health professionals might notice you gained some weight and believe you to be *recovered*. Many people just don't understand that a bit or a lot of weight gain is just the start of the brain's reprogramming work that needs to happen to fully overcome an eating disorder. They don't know that a bit of physical restoration doesn't mean you are free from the addictive and compulsive urges to engage in the eating disorder's behaviours. It's often when you have gained some weight but still have more brain reprogramming work to do that you are likely to need the most support in the process, and this can be when support leaves you. Therefore, it's important that you are assertive and stand up for your needs. Educate people; let them know you are not healed yet. Your body is starting to return to a *healthier* weight, but mentally and emotionally you still have healing to do to become and remain fully free.

# Metabolism

When you have a restrictive eating disorder creating an on-going internal state of energy deficit, it will affect your body's metabolism. People who have restrictive eating disorders often have concerns about their metabolism. Perhaps the most common concern is that they have *broken* their metabolism as a result of keeping their body weight suppressed and chronically under-fuelled.

Let's explore then what the body metabolism is, what it means to have a high or low metabolism and the impact energy deficit can have on it.

### What Is Body Metabolism?

*Metabolism* is a term used to describe all the chemical processes that continuously occur inside your body to keep you alive and functioning at your best. This involves ensuring that your essential organs are working optimally, which include your heart, lungs, gut, kidneys, liver and, very importantly, brain.

In every second of your life, your body is undertaking thousands of chemical reactions to keep your cells functioning and ensure you stay alive.

To keep all these processes running, your body needs essential energy and nutrients, which (in most cases) come from the food and drinks you consume. Your body then breaks these down—which in itself takes energy—to release their energy. This energy is used to keep all your necessary internal functions going, as well as fuelling your day-to-day activities.

**Basal Metabolic Rate**

Even when completely resting, your body is using up calories just to maintain its basic function.

The minimum amount of energy required to carry out these resting chemical processes is called the basal metabolic rate (BMR), and it accounts for anything between 60 and 75 percent of your body's daily energy requirements when you are sedentary. This number is dependent on factors such as age, lifestyle, your body's make-up and your external environment.

**What Happens When Your Body Has Insufficient Energy?**

When your body is starved, meaning the energy being consumed is lower than the energy needed, it loses tissues, including both muscle and fat. This triggers a reduction in your metabolic rate. If your body doesn't have sufficient energy intake, it will try to preserve every bit of energy it does get in any way possible. When it comes to restrictive eating disorders and malnutrition, this is commonly referred to as your body entering *starvation mode*.

When your body enters starvation mode, it aims to stretch out the little energy it does have by turning off nonessential functions and reducing the systems that are still essential to a basic survival level. Examples of how it achieves this include:

- Providing less nutrients to your hair, skin and nails, which become brittle and dry;

- Dropping your heart rate, which is NOT a sign of fitness but a sign of your body trying to stay alive;

- Slowing your gut motility, leading to digestive problems, feeling overly full despite little intake, and constipation; and

- Reducing your body temperature so that you will often feel cold.

This drop in BMR means that your body needs less energy to function and is functioning at a very basic level, ultimately just doing all it can to stay alive.

A drop in BMR can happen when your body's energy intake is dropped for any reason. Therefore, this drop will occur when you eat restrictively or compensate for eating with a restrictive eating disorder. However, the same reduction in metabolism also occurs when people drop their energy intake for reasons such as dieting. In fact, it's this metabolic change that explains why those who do diet are often seen to initially lose weight rapidly (while their metabolism is still at a normal level), but after a couple of weeks of dieting, they find it much harder to sustain the weight they have lost. Essentially, their BMR has dropped so that they are using less baseline energy to function.

When you have a low BMR but then increase your energy intake, your metabolism will respond by beginning to increase. As this happens, your body systems will return to working optimally, which creates an ongoing need for a higher level of energy.

### The Metabolism in Overcoming a Restrictive Eating Disorder

As you overcome a restrictive eating disorder, it's key to abstain from restrictive eating and compensatory behaviours so that you can get your body out of its current state of energy deficit and restore your set point weight. Chapter 9 outlined the symptoms of starvation syndrome, along with an explanation of how necessary weight gain can result in key improvements in both the physiological and psychological complications of semi-starvation.

To gain the full amount of necessary weight needed to get your body out of energy deficit, you will need to increase your dietary intake beyond the level required to meet both your BMR and your daily activities. In fact, your intake needs to increase to meet the demands for both of these AND be enough to restore both fat and lean tissues stores AND establish full internal repairs. For this, you will need an escalating intake of energy, which means lots of food.

**Hypermetabolism When You Are Emerging from Energy Deficit**

Research has found that women who have restrictive eating disorders tend not to gain weight for very long if they are fed the energy requirements of healthy adult women who have never had an eating disorder[4]. Instead, they tend to have much higher energy requirements and need to increase their intake more and more for sustained weight gain. The explanation for this is that people who have had restrictive eating disorders often become hypermetabolic once they increase their energy intake sufficiently. This is when their metabolic rate becomes much higher than the average rate expected for someone of their age and sex.

If you become hypermetabolic and you aren't careful, there's a risk of weight loss, as the faster metabolism puts additional energy needs on your body for it to function at just a baseline level. This can deepen your overall state of energy deficit if you aren't eating enough to match it. When your body becomes hypermetabolic, you will also find that you need a much higher level of energy intake to gain weight than that needed by a *normal* person.

## The Hyperthermic Effect

People with restrictive eating disorders are also regularly seen to become hyperthermic as they begin to eat more and restore their weight. This is where your body converts more of your energy intake into heat than a healthy person does, rather than using the excess intake to build tissues. As a result, during the refeeding process, you are likely to feel hot and sweaty at times. This is commonly worse at night. It isn't unusual for someone going through this process to wake in the night sweating, with soaking sheets.

In comparison, healthy people will generally drop their body temperature at night to preserve energy. It's thought that the hyperthermic effect in someone refeeding and attempting to gain weight to their set point can result in up to 30 percent of their energy intake being lost. In a healthy person, this rate is usually around 14 percent.

## Weight Restoration: Fat vs Fat-Free Mass

For your body to gain enough weight to achieve its set point, it needs to restore fat mass and fat-free mass (or lean tissues). This was covered in more depth earlier in this chapter.

To gain fat-free mass, the energy requirements are several times greater than those needed to gain fat mass, but to reach your body's set point weight and get fully out of energy deficit, it is essential to restore both body mass types. As discussed previously, your body will restore a greater proportion of fat mass before it completely gains and restores the full lean tissue stores needed. This final step in the restoration of essential muscles and tissues takes more energy than was required to establish the gains in fat stores. Therefore, this critical latter stage of weight restoration—completely pulling your body out of energy deficit—can be even harder because it needs even more energy to achieve the same rates of gain made earlier in the process.

## What Happens to the Metabolism After Weight Restoration?

After your body has fully emerged from energy deficit and weight has been restored, your energy requirements will probably remain high for some time. People who are overcoming restrictive eating disorders can be very energy inefficient and need higher calorie intakes when compared to a healthy person. In fact, it isn't uncommon for people in this situation to need up to twice the daily energy intake of a healthy person of the same age and sex just to maintain their weight due to ongoing hypermetabolism. This elevated metabolism can settle down in six months, but it's recommended that you persist with high calorie intake long term for the best chance of keeping your body out of energy deficit and potential relapse.

## What Does This Mean for You?

For anyone overcoming a restrictive eating disorder, this means that once you are providing your body with sufficient energy on a daily basis, your body will increase your metabolism to a higher rate than that seen in healthy individuals. When this happens, your body's energy needs will escalate, and you will need a higher amount of calorie intake to keep gaining weight. As your body reaches the end of the process of restoring all lean tissues, alongside fat mass, your energy needs are likely to be very high.

While you are going through this process, you are probably going to be warm or hot a lot of the time, and you might experience night sweats or clamminess. You might notice a rise in your heart rate. Over time, though, you should also start to notice that your nails, hair and skin are healthier.

Once you have fully weight restored, the level of intake you need each day to maintain your weight and prevent your body from re-entering a state of energy deficit is likely to be significantly higher than healthy people of your age and sex. This higher energy need could continue for a significant amount of time. Therefore, you need to eat without any restriction, which means a lot of food, to escape energy deficit and let your body restore. And you need to keep eating a lot of food, without any restriction, into your future.

**Finally... But Is My Metabolism Broken?**

So then, it's time to address the fear many have, which is whether your metabolism is broken. What if you have been gaining weight while still restricting or still compensating through exercise or other means? What if you are already at a *healthy weight* but still suppressing your true natural size and continuing to restrict? Has this ongoing suppression of your metabolism left it now incapable of repair?

Happily, the answer is that your metabolism is not broken. You can't break your metabolism; it just needs a bit of TLC.

If you have been continuing to restrict your intake and/or exercise but just to a lesser extent, and you have gained some weight, your metabolism has probably remained in starvation mode to preserve the precious extra energy it was given. Your body used the small amount of surplus energy it did receive to build some emergency energy stores as fat because your brain recognised that there was a risk of food becoming scarce once again. It therefore kept your overall metabolism turned down as it didn't feel confident enough to speed the metabolism up when supplies coming in were still lower than it would like. This ongoing low intake indicated to your brain that you were still in an environment of food scarcity.

If this is your situation, things can still change.

You need to eat more now and break the ongoing restriction. Give your body the amount of energy it needs and stop compensating for what you are eating. Do this and your body will respond. Your body will then learn to trust that fuel is in sufficient supply and that it can *afford* to work at an optimal level and turn your metabolism up. Stay consistent with your eating and energy intake without compensating, and your metabolism will heal. As it does, your weight will naturally settle back at your genetic set point, which your body will then fight to maintain.

· · · ●· ● · · ·

# The Neurobiology of Hunger

With a restrictive eating disorder and as you go through the process of overcoming one, there's little doubt that you will think about hunger a lot. Perhaps you debate with yourself as to whether you are hungry or not, whether you are even able to feel your true hunger levels or if you can trust the hunger you do experience. You possibly have questions as to why you get such conflicting messages between your stomach feeling full and your brain sending strong urges to eat, or why it often feels as if your hunger just won't switch off. These questions can create additional unwanted anxiety as you push against the powerful urges to restrict and make yourself eat more.

Understanding more about the processes of hunger and satiety can help. Learning what happens in the brain and body to drive you to eat or to stop eating in normal circumstances—and what's different when you are in a state of energy deficit—will help you make sense of your hunger symptoms.

### What Is Hunger?

In evolutionary terms, hunger served a key purpose. The drive to eat (hunger) would arise from the need to replace energy the body has used and so create a push to find, gather and consume energy-providing foods. In this way, hunger is an evolutionary process that stimulates the drive for food, and it's essential for survival.

Hunger is a conscious sensation, but it isn't experienced by everyone in the same way. There are several hormonal, chemical and neural processes that control hunger and satiety levels. Your brain acts as the central hub for these, turning them on and off according to signals from your body.

The key brain region responsible for controlling hunger is within the hypothalamus. A range of signals relating to hunger and satiety are integrated here and culminate in a response being sent back to your body. Two sets of nerve cells in this part of your brain are responsible for this: the orexigenic neurons, which are responsible for circuits promoting feelings of hunger and stimulating the drive to eat, and the anorexigenic neurons, which are responsible for circuits promoting feelings of satiation that will inhibit (or stop) the drive to eat. Different cues trigger each of these distinct circuits.

**Key Hormones and Chemicals That Trigger the Brain's Hunger and Satiation Circuits:**

- **Ghrelin** is a hormone produced in the gastrointestinal (GI) tract that sends signals to your brain to increase hunger and reduce energy use. Ghrelin therefore creates feelings of physical hunger and promotes stomach contractions, causing *hunger pangs*. Ghrelin is also responsible for stimulating your brain to increase food thoughts to push you to seek food and eat. Ghrelin levels increase as your stomach empties, and when your stomach is filled, ghrelin levels reduce. Ghrelin is also related to an increase in the release of cortisol.

- **Cortisol** is the main stress hormone, and in acute stress it serves to provide your body with enough glucose for instant energy to deal with the stressful situation. It makes sense that cortisol is released with ghrelin as this is your brain recognising that food is needed. To the brain and body, food is life. Therefore, insufficient food is a stressful situation that needs to be addressed, and so cortisol release occurs to help with the hunt for food supplies.

- **Leptin** is a hormone produced exclusively in adipose (fat) cells and acts on receptors in your brain to regulate long-term hunger and food intake. Leptin indicates to your brain the level of your body's total energy stores (as was discussed earlier in this chapter). Low leptin tells your brain there is a shortage in energy supply and that your body is in a state of energy deficit, while elevated leptin indicates more energy stores than are required. Leptin is considered the most powerful appetite-suppressing hormone we have, as it creates feelings of satiety. The more fat cells we have, the more leptin. If there are insufficient or decreasing fat stores, your leptin levels will be low, which can trigger ongoing feelings of hunger and uncontrollable urges to eat. This is an evolutionary survival response, as the key function of leptin is to protect against weight loss below a certain threshold. On the flip side, rising levels of leptin above a threshold level promote biological processes to stimulate weight loss. It's leptin that helps to explain why normal people who diet rarely sustain their diet beyond an initial amount of weight loss. When they lose fat stores below a certain level and their leptin levels decrease, they feel overpowering urges to eat, impossible to resist.

- **Cholecystokinin (CCK)** is produced in the upper small bowel soon after food reaches that part of your GI tract and stimulates a feeling of fullness.

- **Peptide YY** is made in the last part of the small bowel and also stimulates circuits for satiation.

- **Other blood levels—including glucose, amino acids, fatty acids, insulin, glucagon and epinephrin**—all provide the brain with additional information about whether to promote feelings of hunger or satiation in the short term.

In addition to the chemicals and hormones listed above that are involved in hunger and satiation, nerve signals send messages directly from your gut to your brain that tell your brain how stretched your stomach is (by food) and stimulate hunger or satiety accordingly.

Your resting metabolic rate is also believed to be associated with hunger and satiety levels. An elevated metabolic rate created by lean tissues signal to your brain that there is a need for more energy. This also increases your experience of hunger.

**Pleasure Pathways Driving the Desire to Eat**

The other key factor to drive appetite and eating behaviours is your brain's pleasure pathway. In healthy people, eating is a pleasurable experience, and so it overlaps with the brain's reward circuits, causing a release of dopamine. This then drives them to seek pleasure in food in future. The other key pleasure pathway stimulated through eating is the endocannabinoid pathway.

The brain's reward, structural and hormonal circuits closely intertwine so that when the brain senses a need for more energy, it can activate all these processes together to drive the person to find food and eat. This provides optimal chance of survival.

When someone has a restrictive eating disorder, some of the reward and pleasure response systems from eating break down.

**What Happens to Hunger and Satiety in Eating Disorders?**

Firstly, when it comes to hunger and satiety, there is a lot we still don't know. Research is just beginning to reveal much of what's happening in relation to normal hunger, but it's still very much in its infancy in relation to what happens when a person has an eating disorder. Therefore, this information is based on what science has uncovered to date.

People with restrictive eating disorders have elevated levels of ghrelin and cortisol and reduced levels of leptin (1). This is what you would expect since your body is in a chronic state of energy deficit. Your brain perceives this state as a stressful situation and so releases cortisol to stimulate the release of immediate energy to seek food. Ghrelin is released simultaneously to reduce unnecessary energy expenditure, reduce your metabolism and create an increase in food thoughts.

Leptin will be chronically low while your body is in a state of energy deficit because of fat stores that are below the threshold your body requires. This chronically low leptin will create on-going feelings of hunger and a constant drive to eat, even if your stomach is full.

Therefore, hunger systems, on a biological level, are largely working as they should in people with restrictive eating disorders. It's the brain's reward system that explains the ability of people with restrictive eating disorders to override their hunger (1). This is where the addiction to energy deficit becomes more powerful than the biological pleasure experienced in eating foods.

In the brains of people with restrictive eating disorders, dopamine reward pathways are less activated in response to food seeking and eating than they are in healthy people. However, they are activated in response to food aversion behaviours (restriction) and movement or other compensatory behaviours. This makes avoidant behaviours of food stronger as they become more rewarding, addictive and habitual.

All of this means that with a restrictive eating disorder, you will feel hunger in the same way as *healthy people,* but the reward from eating is negated by fear and anxiety to eating behaviours, which are a result of your addiction to restriction. This is a powerful process that overrides the drive to eat enough.

As discussed earlier in the book, people with restrictive eating disorders also have reduced inhibitory control mechanisms in relation to either attempting to stop themselves restricting or impulses to compensate for eating.

In summary then, your ability to override the hunger that arises from the restrictive eating disorder is coming from a combination of a reduced reward response to eating and elevated reward response to food aversion and compensation. This is also tied into a reduced ability to stop yourself from engaging in restrictive or compensatory behaviours.

When you are overcoming a restrictive eating disorder, it's important to start to tune in again to your body. Your body's hunger signals can work normally, and your body has the same hunger and satiety circuits as any *healthy* person. The fact you have been overriding these signals for a long time, though, means that you are out of tune with the messages your body is sending in relation to what it needs when it comes to energy and nutrients.

Recognise, too, that while you remain in a state of energy deficit and below your body's natural set point weight, with insufficient fat stores, your leptin levels will remain below the level at which your brain recognises to be a state of energy balance. While your leptin levels are low, you cannot experience normal satiety, and that ongoing drive to eat—which you almost certainly have (if you are honest!)—will not switch off entirely until your fat stores and leptin levels are sufficient. However, this chronically low leptin, impacting on the inability to feel truly satiated, is also going to be up against competing signals to your brain from your stomach. Therefore, if you have eaten a large meal or huge amount of food, your brain is likely to give you that confusing mix of signals from a full and stretched stomach coupled with an ongoing craving to keep eating. This is going to make your hunger signals a bit whacky for a while as you go through the refeeding process, but go with it. The urges to eat are not your brain or body trying to trick you. Follow them and when your body and leptin levels are restored to your set point level, your hunger will normalise. Trust your body signals, avoid overriding them and keep responding to them.

---

1. https://www.scientificamerican.com/article/unexpected-clues-emerge-about-why-diets-fail/.

2. Dulloo, AG, Miles-Chan, JL & Schutz, Y. Collateral fattening in body composition autoregulation: its determinants and significance for obesity predisposition. Eur J Clin Nutr 72, 657-664 (2018). https://doi.org/10.1038/s41430-018-01 38-6.

3. Dulloo, AG, Miles-Chan, JL & Schutz, Y. Collateral fattening in body composition autoregulation: its determinants and significance for obesity predisposition. Eur J Clin Nutr 72, 657-664 (2018). https://doi.org/10.1038/s41430-018-0138 -6https://www.nature.com/articles/s41430-018-0138-6.

4. Marzola, E, Nasser, JA, Hashim, SA, et al. Nutritional rehabilitation in anorexia nervosa: review of the literature and implications for treatment. BMC Psychiatry 13, 290 (2013). https://doi.org/10.1186/1471-244X-13-290.

# Chapter Eleven

---

# What About Fear of Weight Gain?

I t's time to address the elephant in the room (or book), which is fear of weight gain. For many of you, this is going to be a primary concern. It therefore seemed appropriate to give this topic a chapter of its own even though fear of weight gain isn't, as you have been led to believe, the driving force behind restrictive eating disorders.

For any of you who have skipped through the book to head straight for this section, the following information has been covered in earlier chapters. It will help you to understand this before you read further:

- Restrictive eating disorders are an addiction to energy deficit. This makes any behaviours or food restriction that lead your body into a state of energy deficit highly rewarding and in themselves addictive (see Chapter 2).

- The predisposition to develop an addiction to energy deficit comes from an evolutionary and once much-needed survival-based response to flee a famine situation (see Chapter 7).

- The ancestors from whom the predisposition to the eating disorder evolved were not affected by fears about weight gain. The reason they were driven to avoid energy intake was to enable them to leave the scarce environment they were in and move to an area in which there was much greater food availability. This was to secure their own survival and that of their family members.

- These facts should lead us to question the validity of today's pervasive cultural belief that restrictive eating disorders stem from a powerful fear of weight gain.

In truth, I was never comfortable with the theory that eating disorders are first and foremost due to a fear of weight gain, even though this view is commonplace today. But I will admit that having been subjected to this view throughout the years of having a restrictive eating disorder—even when it didn't feel quite right—I started to believe it. After all, the other theories about eating disorders—such as their being about *control*, arising from perfectionism or poor parenting—made me even more uncomfortable.

As a result of the research I've undertaken and new understanding I've gained from writing this book, I've developed an insight into eating disorders that now makes absolute sense. It fits both with my own experience of having a restrictive eating disorder and my observations from working with countless others. I no longer believe that eating disorders are due to a fear of gaining weight. This is a powerful story that we have all been led to believe for three key reasons:

1. We live in a culture that idolises weight loss.

2. As a result of this culture, many people with restrictive eating disorders do have a strong aversion to the thought of gaining weight.

3. The seemingly irrational and dangerous behaviours that people with eating disorders are so driven to has been a puzzle to experts for a long time. The fear of weight gain theory has been a convenient conclusion to draw.

Some of you reading this are probably now experiencing a resistance to the idea that the eating disorder you have lived with is not purely related to fear of weight gain. It's an understandable reaction if this explanation has been your story for why this awful eating disorder has destroyed your life in all the ways it doubtless has. I'd invite any of you who are facing an inner resistance to this idea to read on with an open mind.

## If Restrictive Eating Disorders Are Not a Fear of Weight Gain, What Drives Them?

It's time to turn the notion that restrictive eating disorders are driven primarily by a fear of weight gain into the reality. They are an addiction to a state of energy deficit. This means that any behaviours you engage in that create energy deficit, which will result in weight loss, become quickly addictive in and of themselves. When your body is in a state of energy deficit, it is by definition below the weight at which it needs to be to function optimally. Therefore, to overcome the eating disorder, returning to a state of energy balance necessitates weight gain.

When you are driven to continue to pursue sometimes dangerous and extreme behaviours that create energy deficit and to resist anything that might lead to energy surplus and weight gain, it's understandable that the natural conclusion has become *I am scared to gain weight.* However, this conclusion has been oversimplified and certainly doesn't fit with the experience of all people with restrictive eating disorders. It was never an explanation that met with my experiences. In recent years, I've also worked with several people for whom fear of weight gain plays no part in their eating disorder experience. Yet they too are just as compelled to remain in a state of energy deficit which keeps their weight low.

In Chapter 8, the presence of eating disorders throughout history was discussed, as well as the prevalence of restrictive eating disorders in people from non-Western cultures today. Wherever restrictive eating disorders have been observed within cultures in which there is no societal pressure to be *thin*, the explanations attributed to the commonly observed *starvation* behaviours differ. In these cases, a fear of weight gain is not considered to play any part.

As humans we like a reason or a story for why something makes us feel the way we do. The fact that stopping eating disordered behaviours leads to weight gain—and people experience strong resistance to doing so—has resulted in a *fear of weight gain* story that seems credible, but it's not quite that simple. The truth is, when a person attempts to stop any addiction to a behaviour or substance, the symptoms of resistance are the same. They just come with a different narrative.

### The Symptoms of Fear Are Real

A restrictive eating disorder causes a powerful anxiety-based resistance to stopping the habitual behaviours and doing anything that could promote energy balance. Restoring energy balance leads to weight gain, and so this anxiety response has been mislabelled as fear of weight gain. However, the true cause of this resistance is that behaviours that lead your body away from your *drug* of energy deficit create intense withdrawal symptoms and cravings for that energy deficit *fix*. These withdrawal symptoms are painful and can feel impossible to tolerate.

Two withdrawal symptoms that you will instantly experience when you are not engaging in your habitual *drug fix* of energy deficit will be anxiety and fear. As discussed in Chapter

3, these arise from the brain's amygdala region, which is the fight-or-flight centre.

If someone who is addicted to a drug is faced with the possibility that they won't be able to access their drug at their habitual time, they will experience a reaction driven by their amygdala of high anxiety and pure fear. It might sound crazy, but this is the same as you can experience if you are unexpectedly offered a large slice of cake. Eating the cake would stop your usual powerful *fix* of energy deficit, which you usually maintain through habitual restrictive eating behaviours. If that fix is threatened, in this case by the cake, you will experience the same instantaneous fear or even panic response as that experienced by the person addicted to a drug.

These primal and brain-based fear reactions you can experience when you are overcoming a restrictive eating disorder—which can be powerful at maintaining it—do not arise from a fear of weight gain. It's a reaction that any person with a strong addiction to anything will experience when not able to pursue their usual *fix*.

The other brain system that contributes to elevated anxiety is the dopamine system, which was also discussed in Chapter 3. As a result of the addiction, your brain has developed a dopamine deficit that creates an internal state of anxiety and depression when you are not engaged in the eating disorder behaviours. The longer you have an eating disorder and engage in related behaviours, the greater your dopamine deficit will be. Not engaging in your usual behaviours creates high levels of anxiety, which can also feel like fear or panic. The only way to reduce this inner anxiety in the long term is by stopping the behaviours and allowing your brain to reprogram. This naturally means weight gain, and so in reality weight gain can be a key factor in alleviating your current chronically anxious state.

Many people who go through the process of overcoming an eating disorder and restoring their natural body weight believe they are terrified of weight gain and that they won't tolerate it. However, as they progress through the process, they are amazed to discover that their fears about weight gain diminish despite being bigger than they have been in years, possibly ever. This is due to the dopamine deficit returning to a level balance. The underlying anxiety, which has been mislabelled as concerns about weight gain, has diminished because dopamine levels are restored to a level that will allow the person to feel calm, even when they are no longer engaging in the eating disorder.

### Avoidance Reinforces a Fear-Based Response

The other way in which a fear response is strengthened over time is avoidance behaviour.

When you have an eating disorder, you might experience an instant fear-based reaction when you attempt to eat a food that is outside your usual level of restriction, such as a burger. This fear reaction arises because eating that burger is not engaging in your addiction. In fact, it could be said eating the burger is the same as abstaining from your usual habit of restriction, which is your *drug*. This pushes your limbic system and amygdala into life because your brain needs its fix. The activated limbic system leads to the high fear response and feelings of panic you then experience. Your brain is programmed to recognise fear and what's caused it. Therefore, your brain registers the cause of this reaction (the burger) and wires it in as a threat that should be avoided in future. Your brain does not understand that this fear is irrational. As far as your brain is concerned, there was fear and so there must have been genuine danger. This leads to increasing levels of fear at even the thought of eating a burger and active future avoidance of such a situation.

The same scenario can occur with anything you have attempted to face with the eating disorder that would compromise your state of energy deficit. If you have avoided high-density foods, certain food types, resting or other behaviours that can lead to an energy surplus, your brain will have labelled them all as potentially dangerous. As a result, your brain will now create a powerful fear response when you encounter them.

### It's Time to Change the Narrative

Many people develop restrictive eating disorders because of dieting behaviours that created an initial energy deficit, triggering their susceptibility. This initial drive to lose weight has been coupled with our cultural view that people *should be smaller*, media reporting of an *obesity epidemic* and other societal pressures that all leave you believing it would be *wrong* to gain weight. This is certainly a very strong, powerful belief system that can make it that bit harder to make the necessary changes to overcome the eating disorder. But these beliefs and fears alone are not the powerful driving force to the eating disorder.

Perhaps changing this internal narrative will help.

You are not as afraid of weight gain as you believe yourself to be. The deep anxiety you experience arising from the eating disorder and the panic that can come when you attempt to overcome it are not stemming from fears of weight gain alone. They arise from a deeply embedded addiction that creates overwhelming withdrawal symptoms of fear and anxiety. These symptoms are so strong, they can be seemingly impossible to tolerate. Have compassion for yourself in relation to this. If overcoming symptoms such as these was easy, then people would overcome eating disorders and other addictions with a lot more ease and much higher success rates than they do.

### The Fear of Weight Gain Belief Can Become Self-Fulfilling

At the end of the day, continuing to believe the fear of weight gain narrative could be harmful.

Beliefs too often become self-fulfilling prophecies. For example, *I believe I have no confidence, so I act like someone with no confidence,* or *I believe that I'm scared of gaining weight, and so I act like someone who is scared of gaining weight.* These beliefs become your identity, and this identity then disempowers you and lessens your ability to change. This reinforces the belief, and it becomes a vicious and self-fulfilling cycle.

I don't think you are scared of gaining weight, not to the level you believe yourself to be. Once you stop acting like you are and start working through the difficult process of abstaining from the eating disordered behaviours— decisively pursuing behaviours that take you away from energy deficit, even though they will result in weight gain—you will also finally realise that this is something you can indeed cope with.

# Chapter Twelve

# Quasi-Recovery or Addicted to Moderation?

T he majority of you have probably heard and used the term *quasi-recovery* before. A definition is provided below for anyone who is unfamiliar with the term and to ensure we are all of the same understanding when we refer to it. This is what I consider *quasi-recovery* to be:

> *Quasi-recovery is a term commonly used in eating disorder communities. It relates to when you have made some progress along the trajectory of over-coming an eating disorder, where fully consumed by the eating disorder is at one end and fully free of it is at the other. Despite your progress, it has now stalled, and you are currently treading water. Prior*

*to this, you made some changes to overcome the eating disorder. Food intake became less restrictive, and other compensatory behaviours or rituals either reduced, switched or stopped. Mental and physical shifts have occurred, but you are by no means at your potential in terms of fully overcoming the eating disorder and living a life free from it.*

If you are living in what could be considered *quasi-recovery,* you are likely to argue that you are now eating more than you were, yet your intake remains restrictive to your body's needs and your hunger. You have possibly gained some weight, and so you and the people around you might consider you to be *better,* but you remain below your set point, have not allowed for overshoot and remain in an energy deficit state. Because you aren't engaging in exercise as much as you were or perhaps you have replaced purging with daily yoga, you have managed to convince others that things are better. However, you are still driven by the compulsions that remain or by those you have switched to.

In a quasi-recovered state, you might be engaging in life with work, studies and other pursuits, but it's likely to be in quite a structured and habitual way, with raised anxiety if your routine is threatened. Finding pleasure in life remains a challenge to you; spontaneity is incredibly hard, the concept of fun largely unknown. Overall, in quasi-recovery, you still have an active eating disorder and continue to live a narrow and addicted life.

In this *quasi*-state you will also resist making any more changes that will impact on your ability to pursue your usual *fix* of energy deficit because that fix is so numbing and calming.

There are two ways you can reach a point of quasi-recovery.

The first is that you begin the process to try to overcome the eating disorder using a moderation approach, such as with a meal plan, and then you never move beyond it.

The second is that you jump into an abstinence approach but only last a matter of weeks or months before some of the old urges and compulsions overpower you again.

Effectively, in *quasi-recovery*, you still have an addiction to energy deficit and a very active eating disorder. It's manifesting differently but needs to be recognised for what it is. Your restrictive intake might not be as significant as it has been in the past, but what remains is just as addictive. There may be less compensatory behaviours or a change from one type to another, but those that are still present remain just as compulsive. The addiction to a state of energy deficit is still present; it just has different behavioural patterns driving it, and it's still life limiting. You have effectively adapted the eating disordered behaviours and continue to engage in them at a *moderated* level.

When you continue to engage with the addictive behaviours, even in a moderated way, you are still creating a deeper dopamine deficit in your brain. You are also continuing to use and strengthen the deeply embedded eating disordered brain networks, not allowing them to be unwired and replaced by circuits driving healthier behaviours. In this way, quasi-recovery is a state of being addicted to moderation.

In other addictions and even in eating disorders, reduced engagement with the *drug*, applying moderation, is a tool used by medical teams to minimise the risk of harm that can arise from them. Unfortunately, this doesn't take from the fact that the overall addiction remains, massively impacting on quality of life. While the eating disorder is still active, there is also an ongoing and significant risk of further decline.

When you are addicted to slightly moderated but still compelling eating disordered behaviours, trying to stay afloat and not slide back can be exhausting. It's less exhausting to be fully entrenched in the eating disorder. When you are, you don't have to apply conscious thought; you just follow the compulsively driven, miserable but numbing habits. On the flip side, fully engaging in overcoming the eating disorder through abstinence is also less exhausting because you are in a determined, *going for it*, state of mind. In *quasi-recovery* and when stuck in a life of moderation, a lot more mental effort is necessary as you aim to eat restrictively but not *too restrictively* or allow yourself to engage in some compensatory behaviours but prevent them from escalating. This can be a constant juggling act, all while also having to present to the world a functioning, smiling, capable person, despite feeling like you are crumbling inside.

If you can identify with this state of being, take heart. You have left the starting line and proven to yourself that you can make changes. Maybe now the time is right to get from where you are to the end of the line and finally fully overcome the eating disorder. So, how do you do that?

You do so in the same way as anyone who wants to fully overcome a restrictive eating disorder. You apply abstinence to all your behaviours and restrictive eating. You seek support and pull on any resources you can find. You trust yourself and your abilities, develop skills in self-empowerment and new coping skills for when life gets tough, which it will.

Studies carried out on people with alcohol and drug dependence demonstrate that those who have overcome an addiction through abstinence have a higher quality of life and greater feelings of self-trust and self-worth than those who have recovered using a moderation approach[1]. It's beyond a doubt that this is true for people with eating disorders too.

---

1. Subbaraman MS, Witbrodt J. Differences between abstinent and non-abstinent individuals in recovery from alcohol use disorders. Addict Behav. 2014 Dec; 39(12): 1730-5. doi: 10.1016/j.addbeh.2014.07.010. Epub 2014 Jul 15. PMID: 25117850; PMCID: PMC4164587.

# Chapter Thirteen

---

# Relapses, Lapses & Pre-Lapses

*Pre-lapse, lapse, relapse...* These terms represent different stages in which you might have slid backwards in the process of overcoming an eating disorder or after you have fully overcome it.

### Relapse

Let's first explore the term that most people are familiar with. A relapse, in relation to an addiction or eating disorder, is when you have all but overcome the addictive disorder but then return to fully using your *drug*.

With a restrictive eating disorder, you might have fully abstained from all the eating disorder habits for a prolonged period and no longer have cravings or withdrawal symptoms. You will be fully out of energy deficit and have restored to your set point weight. A lot of the brain circuitry driving the eating disordered behaviours has been unwired from the old habits, and new habits have wired in that are now automatic. Your dopamine deficit has restored to a healthy level. All this taken together indicates that you have fully overcome an eating disorder, mentally as well as physically. A relapse can be said to have occurred when you are at this *recovered* point but then you re-enter a state of energy deficit, triggering a new, positive reward response. This response pushes you back into the pursuit of those previously addictive behaviours and further *fixes* that energy deficit creates.

A relapse is defined as a full-blown return to the addictive or eating disorder and can occur months, years or even decades after you have overcome it.

### Lapse

Lapses are less significant than a full relapse. An example of a lapse is if you have all but overcome an addictive or eating disorder but start dabbling again in your *drug* and then quickly realise it and abstain. Lapses are lower in risk and can be used as learning opportunities. For example, if you have a lapse due to a stressful life event, it can be a warning sign that better stress management tools and support systems are needed for when the next inevitable life stress hits.

The term *lapse* can also be used when you take a backward step in pursuit of fully overcoming the eating disorder. The term *relapse* in this case is not appropriate, because for a relapse you should first have reached a recovered state. Therefore, in the process of overcoming an eating disorder, a lapse is when you have made good progress but then find that your urges and cravings become stronger, luring you back into a higher level of engagement in the addictive behaviours, which in turn creates a deeper energy deficit. Lapses in the process of overcoming any addiction or eating disorder are natural and common. They are part of the process, but each time they happen, it's key to notice as soon as possible, learn from them and move forwards, putting extra measures in place to prevent the same thing from recurring.

## Pre-lapse

*Pre-lapse* is a less commonly used term but is important to be aware of. A pre-lapse is occurring when some of your thought patterns are beginning to revert but before your behaviours have followed. The stage of pre-lapse can begin a reasonable time before you engage in the old behaviours again, or it can precede a faster descent back to the destructive pursuit of energy deficit.

Increasing thoughts such as these are a sign of a pre-lapse when you have an eating disorder:

- *Surely it can't hurt to lose a couple of pounds now.*

- *I don't think I need that bag of crisps today with my sandwich for lunch because I'm going out for dinner tonight.*

- *Maybe I will take up long-distance cycling. I'm sure it can't hurt when during the eating disorder, it was running I was addicted to.*

These thoughts indicate the onset of new cravings for a hit of energy deficit and are a sign of pre-lapse. If this is not addressed, it could lead to a lapse or full relapse.

Other signs that can be an indication of a pre-lapse include:

- Increasing irritability or anger;

- Becoming more defensive about certain behaviours or habits or being increasingly dishonest with yourself or loved ones;

- Signs of depression or low mood;

- More negative thoughts or an increasingly pessimistic outlook on life;

- Becoming increasingly busy and on the go, not allowing yourself to stop mentally and/or physically; and

- Disengaging from support systems that you have in place.

Remaining mindful and aware of your inner state of both mind and being is important during the process of overcoming an eating disorder and afterwards. This will help to ensure that any signs of possible lapse or relapse are recognised and addressed quickly, as the slope back can be very slippery.

## Recognising the Signs of Pre-lapse, Lapse and Relapse Within Restrictive Eating Disorders

Recognising pre-lapses, lapses and even full relapses can be challenging when you have a restrictive eating disorder. For someone with a gambling or substance use disorder, it is easier to identify a lapse or relapse when, even if they are the only one who knows, the fact that they have had a drink, taken their drug or gambled is clearer cut. Eating disorder behaviours that create energy deficit, which is your *drug*, can be much more insidious. Behaviours can be harder to identify, as can whether your body has re-entered a state of energy deficit.

For example, you might have started to opt for more lower-density foods than you were before, creating a higher energy deficit. However, because you are still eating as frequently, and on the surface food portions don't appear to be significantly smaller, the fact they are more restrictive is less apparent. Exercise and movement for most are a part of life. When you are overcoming an eating disorder, it takes significant self-awareness to identify when movement is the result of a compulsion and when it isn't. Recognising this is not always easy, and, as with restriction, compulsive movement can easily escalate in new ways, which creates a deeper level of soothing energy deficit again. These things can all happen without you or those around you realising that the risk of entering a full relapse is imminent.

You need to remain vigilant and self-aware to identify any signs of pre-lapse, lapse or relapse as soon as possible. This involves recognising your thought patterns and questioning your motives for food choices if they appear to be even slightly more restrictive. Decisions about taking up more exercise or even yoga classes should be explored and reflected upon as to what's really creating this urge to move more. To stay safe as you overcome the eating disorder, honesty with yourself and with those in your support network is going to be invaluable.

Once your body is out of energy deficit, you will need to make every effort to keep it safely in energy balance and avoid anything that will risk it sliding back into that energy deficit state again. This means eating more than you think is enough and not engaging in higher levels or new types of movement or exercise until you are ready to slowly experiment with it in the future. This should only be attempted after you are sure your body has fully restored all your fat and lean tissue stores, and you have given enough time to maintain your set point weight. You should also ensure that you have had a prolonged period without any eating-disorder-driven thoughts or cravings to be as certain as possible that the necessary brain reprogramming work has taken effect.

Remembering and regularly reminding yourself just how awful life in the eating disorder was and what pushed you into the painful process of attempting to overcome it is another key tool in helping to prevent lapses and relapses. Many people relapse or fail to continue with their efforts to overcome an eating disorder because they forget how miserable they were with it.

The rose-tinted glasses go on, removing the memories of the cold, starved, driven and lonely days they lived in the narrow existence of the eating disorder. Find ways to remind yourself what pushed you to pursue the process to overcome the eating disorder so that you aren't tripped up by thoughts like *It wasn't that bad.*

### What Is Happening in Your Brain When You Have a Relapse?

When you learnt about the process of *deep learning* to over-come an eating disorder in Chapter 4, you might well have been left with the impression that once you have abstained from your *drug* for an extended period, your brain circuitry will be fully rewired, making relapse unlikely. This is true to an extent, but unfortunately, some weeds from the old brain network that drove the eating disorder will linger.

As you now know, to learn new things, the connections or synapses between the neurons that drive the new learning form bonds with one another. The more times the new learning is pursued, the stronger the synapses become, creating brain path-ways and networks that make it easier to pursue automatical-ly. At the same time, the connections between the neurons for habits that are no longer being pursued become weakened and depleted in number. In this way the brain circuits for old habits will *unwire*.

However, in someone who has a history of an eating disorder or addiction, it's thought that although there might not be active or conscious pursuit of the old circuits, the circuits can still be activated. It could be that at night you have dreams in which you are engaging in some of your old eating disorder behaviours or when you had a smaller body. Perhaps you occasionally notice someone or see an influencer who is pursuing a life that is very *health driven* or fitness focused. You deem them to have a perfect and happy life and feel a fleeting moment of regret or sadness that this is not you. These thoughts, emotions and subconscious dreams can prevent the old synapses and circuits from fully breaking down. While the old synapses are still present, if the right triggers come along, there is a risk of them becoming reactivated and stronger.

The other factor that makes an eating disordered brain circuit incredibly strong and hard to fully remove is the power of the emotional and pleasure response that created it. The floods of dopamine and other brain chemicals that occurred when you were pursuing the eating disordered circuits made for incredibly powerful *fertiliser* as your brain formed the synapses between those neurons. These connections are likely to be stronger than any that your brain creates, and it may not be possible to fully break them down, leaving some lingering *weeds* that present a degree of risk.

For anyone with the genetic susceptibility to a restrictive eating disorder, entering a state of prolonged energy deficit in future is also a lifelong risk to reigniting those old circuits. Any energy deficit beyond a key point in someone susceptible can switch back on the evolutionary *flee from famine* response. This is a key risk factor to relapse that you will need to stay very mindful of, deliberately pursuing a lifestyle that keeps you safely away from any degree of energy deficit.

• • • ● • ● • • •

# Preventing Relapse -
# Do You Need to Abstain for Life?

It's only natural that when you have lived through something as distressing and life changing as a restrictive eating disorder and been through the difficult process of overcoming it, you will have a genuine concern about the possibility of relapse. These fears are a good thing because they will help you develop self-awareness and tools to minimise your risk.

One key question is whether abstinence for life is necessary in relation to the eating disorder habits you had. Or, once the addictive nature of those old habits is seemingly overcome, is it possible to return to some of those behaviours in a moderated way? As detailed throughout the book, when it comes to a restrictive eating disorder, the overarching addiction is to the state of energy deficit. And this is something that, once corrected, you should avoid at all costs in future.

### Ongoing Abstinence from Energy Deficit

Even after overcoming a restrictive eating disorder, your brain will remain easily triggered by energy levels in your body when it's choosing which neural networks to follow. If your brain recognises that your body is in a stable energy balance or even surplus, it will see this as a signal to continue to follow the new circuits you have built. However, returning to a state of energy deficit can trigger your brain to follow those old, lingering circuits, as the energy deficit state was such a powerful past trigger. Your brain will remember that when your body was in that state before, those old pathways were safe and rewarding to pursue. This means that re-entering any level of energy deficit will stimulate your old brain pathways and the release of those seductive and alluring brain chemicals (endorphins and dopamine), making the pursuit for more an attractive option.

This is why the best way to prevent future relapse for someone who carries a genetic susceptibility to a restrictive eating disorder is to avoid any risk of re-entering a state of energy deficit. Dieting and extreme exercise kicks, although perhaps safe for others to dabble in, are not something that someone who has overcome a restrictive eating disorder should ever consider. Consuming less energy than your body needs or expending more than your body can afford to use will always risk your re-entering a state of energy deficit and triggering your biological susceptibility.

Of course, entering a state of energy deficit isn't always something you can have full control over. Some people re-enter a negative energy balance because of physical illness, and this is sufficient to *restart* the addictive pull of the eating disorder. One way to protect against this is to ensure that both you and your loved ones are aware of this risk. If physical illness does hit, doing everything possible to ensure that sufficient forms of nutritional energy are still coming into your body will be vital. If you are not well enough to advocate for this yourself, then ensure that your loved ones know enough to be able to advocate on your behalf.

Abstaining from energy deficit for life, as far as is feasibly possible, is going to decrease your risk of relapse throughout your future. But what about the other behaviours that were part of the eating disorder and in themselves became so addictive as they enabled you to get your fix from energy deficit? Can you engage in a moderated way in any of these old behaviours again?

When you think about the typical behaviours that make up a restrictive eating disorder, perhaps the main one that you might want to pursue in your future is movement and exercise. I think we can agree that most of the others—such as purging through vomiting, use of laxatives or compulsively weighing yourself—are not entirely necessary to include in a fulfilling and healthy future life.

### Exercise and Movement in Moderation

When it comes to exercise, can you engage in this again after overcoming the addiction to it?

The answer to this is yes, as long as it's pursued with self-awareness, observing for any old patterns that could emerge or stronger urges to pursue more. It's also advisable that you don't begin to engage in any of the old addictive behaviours again too soon. Ensure you have allowed sufficient time for full brain reprogramming to have taken place and for your body to have fully emerged from energy deficit and settled at your set-point weight, in a state of energy balance. If you find yourself feeling agitated and anxious for the green light to return to exercise, perhaps reflect on where this agitation is coming from. This is a potential red flag, as it indicates that your brain still has some dependence on and urgent need for your old *drug*. See this as a sign that it's too soon to engage in more movement again yet.

Once you have given plenty of time for your body and brain to adjust as you fully overcome the eating disorder, you do have the option of experimenting again with some forms of movement or exercise that you want to enjoy into your future.

If you decide to pursue previously compulsive forms of exercise or movement, it's worth, especially at the beginning, setting strict limits. Decide how much you will do and how often. Find ways to remain accountable to this.

Self-binding strategies can help moderate the amount of willpower you need to not pursue more than might be sensible. These strategies establish black-and-white limits that you have decided on in advance. If you do re-engage in exercise or movement, stay self-aware. When you notice urges to go further than the limits you have set, recognise this is happening and perhaps abstain again for a while. Sometimes your brain needs a bit more time to unwire those old brain circuits, and it's worth giving it this time to ensure that the risk of your sliding back is minimal.

Another consideration is the type of movement or exercise you engage in in future. It's possible that the old brain circuits that were so strongly embedded may never *unwire* completely, and some weeds will always linger. Therefore, pursuing behaviours that were once such a strong part of the eating disorder too soon, or in some cases ever, could be enough to reactivate those old circuits and push them quickly back into life. On the other hand, if you choose an alternative movement-based pursuit that was never part of the original eating disorder, the risk of reactivating the old circuits will be lower. For example, if during the eating disorder, you had a strong addiction to running, then running again might be too great a risk, whereas other forms of movement are safer.

Engaging again in any forms of movement or exercise after you have overcome an eating disorder is something to do with care and even more so if you choose to return to exercise types that you were previously highly addicted to.

Just because you can safely engage in some of those previously highly compulsive behaviours again doesn't mean that you must. Some people find that when they do overcome the eating disorder and their brain is fully reprogrammed, the desire to engage in any of those old behaviours disappears completely. For example, people who used to be high achievers in their choice of sport—and thought they would have a drive to engage in it again as soon as it was safe—actually find, when they overcome the eating disorder, their desire to go back to it is not just gone; they now have a strong aversion to the thought of doing so.

For others, the desire to engage again in those old pursuits remains, but when they do go back to it, they find that they derive absolutely no pleasure from it. This is not an uncommon phenomenon in people who have overcome other addictions too. People who have abstained from their *drug* for a lengthy period and then go back to it describe being surprised to find it does nothing for them.

For some, movement and exercise will form part of your future, and you will engage in moderate amounts happily and safely. For others, the drive to do so will be minimal. Either situation is okay. As long as the eating disorder is gone and behaviours are no longer compulsive or addictive, you get to decide whether pursuing movement-based activities is something you want to do. Some will, but others will prefer less active hobbies and interests, in the same way people who have never had eating disorders do.

### Future Abstinence from Restriction

When it comes to your future and your nutritional intake, it will be vital to ensure your nutrition is always sufficient, without restricting food types or amounts. Restricting food intake in any form would not be sensible in your future. As life is far more interesting and satisfying when eating without restriction, the future deliberate pursuit of restrictive eating is unlikely to hold much appeal! However, one method to protect against future energy deficit arising from insufficient food intake is to have a *safety net* amount of food that you eat daily as an absolute minimum, no matter what. This doesn't need to be a calorie limit but a general impression in your mind's eye of how much food, as a minimum, it takes each day to satisfy your body's needs, maintain energy balance (and a stable weight) and keep you mentally and physically healthy. This minimum safety net is something you can fall back on if illness or times of high stress or anxiety impact on your appetite or your future ability to eat.

## Managing Future Life Events and Stressful Events

Future life events and stressful situations can be triggers that stimulate a relapse in someone with a history of an eating disorder. There can be triggers in months or even years from now for which the response your brain knows is the old addictive circuitry that has been dormant but isn't fully broken down.

People who face a significant stressful event in their life, such as a bereavement or a traumatic situation, can find that they are automatically pursuing those old eating disorder behaviours again in the aftermath. This is because their brain has not yet faced such a highly emotive situation in the time since they overcame the eating disorder. Their brain still remembers, *When huge life stress occurs, we restrict / exercise / purge or generally pursue energy deficit to feel better.*

This same response can occur from extremes of emotion at either end of the spectrum, so you have a similar risk when incredible things happen that spark waves of positive emotions and not just with distressing and painful experiences. It's of course very hard to prepare for these situations, but as with anything, insight is key. When life events do come along that are either very stressful or highly emotive in positive or negative ways, be aware they could push you automatically back into old habits. This can happen no matter how long it has been since you overcame the eating disorder or how strong you feel in having beaten it. Use your safety net at these times for food intake and be mindful of any urges to engage again in old compensatory behaviours or actions that will lead you back to energy deficit.

The intention of this section is not to make you feel that you will always have to be on your guard or hypervigilant to the risk of relapse. Nor is it to say that fully overcoming an eating disorder is not possible.

Most people who fully overcome eating disorders develop excellent self-awareness in the process and are so insightful when it comes to the dangers of diet culture and the *thin-ideal* that this alone makes them largely bulletproof to the risks of relapse. They live lives in which re-entering a state of energy deficit is an incredibly low risk because they wouldn't entertain the idea of re-engaging in any form of restrictive eating or behaviours that could take them back there. And the longer they stay positive and committed to their free future, the more strongly their brains have reprogrammed, with higher likelihood that the old brain circuits are pruned out. So, please don't take the information in this section as disheartening. You can fully overcome the eating disorder and live a free future life. However, putting some sensible measures into that future life to keep you healthy is no bad thing if it helps to ensure the eating disorder stays where it belongs...deeply buried in your past!

# Chapter Fourteen

---

# And Finally...
# Take-Home Tips
# to Overcome an
# Addiction to Energy
# Deficit

**P** rioritise

All too often people fail to make progress in overcoming an eating disorder and the highly addictive power it holds because they just don't appreciate the amount of mental energy, focus and time involved. If the process was as simple as increasing your food intake and resting a bit more while still pursuing everything else that life is demanding of you—such as work, studies, family commitments and household chores—then people would overcome eating disorders every day, and you wouldn't be reading this book. I hope if you have learnt anything from the information in these pages, it's that your brain has a powerful addiction that it will forcefully pull you to pursue unless you are consciously focused on stopping yourself from habitually following it. The level of conscious focus required takes incredible mental effort. This is not even all you are up against. You will also experience emotions that are painful and that you haven't let yourself go near for years. You will have to learn to sit with and tolerate them on this journey. That isn't something you can easily do while also trying to focus on a job, studies or showing up for the world in other ways. Therefore, make this process to overcome the eating disorder your number one priority every single day in the short term. Block your calendar of other commitments so that you can get through this. Once you are free of the eating disorder, life opens up in more remarkable ways than you can even begin to realise now. You don't want to deny that reality for yourself any longer than you must.

**Aim for Overshoot!**

Chapter 4 gave reasons why the abstinence approach is the best method to overcome a restrictive eating disorder and addiction to energy deficit. Chapter 10 explained why your body needs to go through a process of *fat overshoot* to fully emerge from a state of energy deficit and complete all the restoration and repairs needed. Therefore, combine these two facts and deliberately aim for overshoot. In doing so, you will be taking on a mindset that will allow your brain to more completely reprogram, unwire the eating disordered behaviours and wire in ways of eating and living that will take you to a free life. And, at the same time, you will be giving your body the best chance of healing and restoring. The additional benefit to this approach is that aiming for overshoot helps you to develop skills in body acceptance and gives you a greater appreciation for the positive things that a bigger body will bring you.

## Accept That Extreme Levels of Hunger Are Normal and Respond

You will have learnt in Chapter 10 the reasons that people who have been through a period of semi-starvation and who are in a state of energy deficit (at ANY weight) will experience extremely high levels of hunger. This is a normal physiological response to insufficient stores of fat and lean tissue in relation to the level your body needs. It's not unusual for this hunger to drive you to eat in excess of 10,000 calories a day if you listen to it. This is a normal body doing what it needs to do for survival. Accept your high hunger, learn to listen to it and recognise it as a clear indication that your body remains in a state of energy deficit and needs more energy intake, i.e., food. The high hunger will die down as your body reaches a state of energy balance and has sufficient leptin (a hormone that is key in regulating appetite).

### Don't Try to Control the Rate of Weight Gain or How Much Weight You Gain. Be Proud of Your Body

When you decide that you will let yourself gain some weight but try to do so in a controlled way—manipulating how fast you gain or hitting a certain weight and then pulling back—you do not let go of the eating disorder. This approach leaves you continuing to engage in behaviours that pursue the *hit* of energy deficit your brain craves. If you try to control the rate of gain, you will still have to restrict your food intake or engage in compensatory behaviours, even if it's less than it was previously. This will interfere with your brain's ability to fully reprogram. When you hit a certain weight and then pull back, not only do you hold on to your behaviours and addiction to energy deficit, but you also keep your body from ever reaching a space of being fully healed and as healthy as it can be for you. Instead, allow the weight gain to happen as fast as it needs to and to the level it needs to reach. Avoid looking at the scales. Eat to your hunger, however high. Rest your body as much as you can. While doing these things, work on your body acceptance and even develop pride in your body. Using a coach or professional to help with this can be beneficial.

### Be Prepared for an Emotional Roller Coaster

There are so many ways in which the process of overcoming a restrictive eating disorder is emotionally painful and challenging. Many of these have been explored throughout the book. There is the dopamine deficit you will have to go through, creating painful emotions and withdrawal symptoms. You will have anxiety and fear reactions as you make the important changes you need to make. There is the weight gain to tolerate and emotions to process related to your changing body and accepting it in a bigger size. For some of you there will be past trauma or painful experiences that the eating disorder has numbed and blocked for years that you will need help to address and work through. At the same time, positive emotions can also resurface, which can also feel overwhelming at times. You can feel exhilarated when you achieve a big win over the eating disorder, and it can be an impactful moment when you find yourself genuinely laughing for the first time in what could be years or decades. The emotional roller coaster can be intense in this process, and you will need to be prepared for it, seek support, and build new ways of coping so that you don't race back to old behaviours when it all feels too hard.

### Recognise the Eating Disordered Thoughts and Anxieties for What They Are: Powerful Withdrawal Symptoms and Cravings

When the thoughts come up time and time again, trying to convince you to restrict your intake, hold back on the weight gain, go for that innocent walk or purge but *definitely for the last time,* recognise these thoughts for what they are. When the anxiety rises as you contemplate eating more than your usual restrictive amount, eating at a different time of day or putting on your pyjamas rather than your trainers, recognise it for what it is. The thoughts trying to forcefully pull you towards old behaviours are convincing and can even seem rational when you experience them. The fear and anxiety that come up from making changes are intense at times and can be hard to tolerate. Remind yourself that these thoughts and high levels of anxiety are normal and to be expected. These are withdrawal symptoms and cravings from and for your *drug*. They will reduce and eventually disappear but only if you persist with abstaining from the very things your brain is desperately trying to pull you towards. You will need to have strategies in place to help you resist when the urges become overwhelming.

### Empowering Yourself, Developing Self-trust and Belief in Your Abilities Is Key

Chapter 6 covered the topic of self-empowerment and why your own empowerment to beat this eating disorder is going to make all the difference in terms of how much meaningful progress you ultimately make. Being told what to do and only doing it because someone has asked you to or doing so for the sake of others won't help you reprogram your brain in all the necessary ways. You need to make the changes for you, deciding what you will do, be motivated to do so and push forwards. You need to develop trust in your abilities and belief in yourself. This doesn't mean you go it alone without support, but you take control of the process and you own it—because your future is at stake. When you begin to take hold of your own power to resist those urges and progress, you will feel stronger, which in itself is empowering and powerful!

**Connect with Others and Seek Support. Resist the Urges to Isolate**

Another topic that has come up regularly throughout the book is how important connection with others is. Humans were never supposed to live in isolation. When we are going through hard times, we are meant to seek support and care from others. It might be that you have isolated yourself significantly in the time you have had an eating disorder and you believe there is no one to offer you that connection and support now. This is not the case. Even if you don't have any meaningful relationships now with family or friends, there are people out there you who will want to support you. Forming those connections will make you stronger. It will help you stay on track when things get hard and can give you accountability. And it will give you a sense that you are not as alone as you think you are and there are things worth building a better future for.

**Abstain from Everything Together. Avoid the Risks from Multiple Addictive Behaviours**

When you abstain from one aspect of the eating disorder but not others, you run the risk that the other behaviours will worsen and make abstaining from the one you have chosen to stop even harder to address. When you engage in any of the addictive behaviours to pursue your *drug* of energy deficit, it fires the entire eating disordered brain network into life, dopamine starts pumping out in pursuit of more, and it becomes much harder to stop yourself engaging in any of your old habits. As an example, you decide that you will eat more but continue walking. You might have a bigger breakfast (great), but then you go for your usual habitual walk. This fires up the networks in your brain that are so deep and strong in relation to the eating disorder. Dopamine floods in and you feel calm and great from being out walking and getting your *drug* hit. Suddenly you face urges to walk even farther than normal, thinking you must make up for breakfast. When you get home, the bigger lunch you planned no longer seems a good idea, and you resort back to your safe and habitual restrictive foods. The best approach is always to abstain from everything together. It's easier, not harder in the long run. Give your brain the very best chance to reprogram in full.

### Develop a Self-identify Beyond That of an Eating Disorder

The final tip in this list is something else to focus on as you overcome the eating disorder. Chapter 5 covered the importance of self-identity and how this can impact on the way you perceive yourself and your self-belief. With an eating disorder, so much of your identity becomes tied up in it. You lose sense of who you are and come to believe that you are the person who eats *healthily*, loves exercise or being busy, is driven and self-controlled. The reality is that these are all pure symptoms of a powerful addiction to energy deficit and not who you are. To overcome the eating disorder, you need to let go of this self-identity it has created within you. When you do, it's very likely you will go through a time of feeling a little bit lost, as if you are in a no-man's land, unsure who you are without it. But make that space and use it to gradually let your true self emerge. The person who has a passion for life and interests that have nothing to do with the pursuit of energy deficit, someone who has the capacity to love, laugh and enjoy all sorts of incredible pursuits freely and happily. A person who is strong, empathetic and brave. One method you can use to help you while you develop your new sense of identity away from the eating disorder is to build a picture of that future you. Create a real mental image of who you will become, how it will feel and allow that future you imagine to pull you towards it.

# Chapter Fifteen

# You've Got This!

For anyone who has made it to the conclusion of this book, thank you. I hope there has been some information in these pages that will make a difference to you as you overcome a restrictive eating disorder yourself or support someone else to do so.

At the end of the day, the process of overcoming an eating disorder can be one of incredible self-discovery. You learn how to listen to your needs, physically as well as in all other aspects of life, and to respond to them. This involves ongoing reflection and the development of skills in self-awareness. It's a time in which you need to learn how to be true to yourself so you become self-empowered and can advocate for your needs. Through the process you will come to understand that asking for help is a strength, not a weakness.

As you evolve on your journey, you will learn who you are beyond the eating disorder identity that has consumed you for years or decades. Whoever that person is, they will be stronger and able to experience life in more vital and incredible ways than ever. Any relationships that stand the test of time will be strengthened as you are able to give so much more to those people who are important to you. Your skills in empathy and understanding of others will be powerful.

Overcoming an eating disorder will ensure that you have skills in managing stress and intense emotions in ways that don't involve resorting to harmful habits or addictions.

The eating disorder will have taught you so much about yourself, life and human vulnerabilities. It will give you an appreciation for all the small things in life. The process of overcoming the eating disorder will also enable you to live more authentically than most people ever find the courage to.

Open the door in your mind to the possibility of overcoming the eating disorder, and the opportunities to move beyond it will present themselves. You then have to grab them and put in the action.

Overcoming a restrictive eating disorder is not an easy process. It's a journey that takes time and changes that will feel like great sacrifices in the moment. Emotionally, it's likely to be the most challenging thing you ever do. There will be days when you will feel like you can't go on, but you can and you will. Slowly you will evolve through it, and all the pain, the discomfort and the sacrifice will finally be worth it.

# Want More Tips?

If you found this book informative and helpful then you might be interested in my second book, *Aiming For Overshoot.*

*Aiming for Overshoot* is a handbook for anyone overcoming a restrictive eating disorder, providing even more practical information, hints, tips, motivation, inspiration and encouragement to aim for overshoot, fully reprogram your brain, restore your body and most importantly, find your eating disorder free life!

# About the Author

Helly Barnes is a professional coach for people overcoming restrictive eating disorders. She uses neuroscience, research, her personal history with an eating disorder and her professional experience to provide an informed approach and empower anyone to overcome the destructive and addictive nature of an eating disorder.

Helly now lives an unconventional life, following her heart. She considers herself a full-time nomad and she is never happier than when travelling the world and appreciating all it has to offer.

# Useful Links to the Author

While in the process of overcoming a 14-year-history of a restrictive eating disorder, Helly kept a blog of her experiences still available at:

www.recoveringnomad.com

And Helly writes a regular blog today on her coaching website:

www.hellybarnes.com

You will also find more information and ramblings by Helly on her podcast series,

*Feck it, Fun, Fabulous and Free in Eating Disorder Recovery,*

which is freely available on all mainstream podcasting platforms.

Made in United States
Troutdale, OR
11/10/2023